woman food

woman food

Jody Vassallo
Dell Stanford BSc SRD

photography by
Deirdre Rooney

MURDOCH
B O O K S

contents

eating for optimum health

Women are constantly being bombarded with conflicting information about diet and health, so it's easy to get confused about exactly what foods should be part of a healthy diet. The aim of this book is to provide up-to-date, credible and 'fad-free' information on the role of diet in the health and well-being of women.

The following pages show you how to eat the right balance of foods for optimum health. As a woman's body changes throughout life, so do her nutritional needs. The physical demands of menstruation, pregnancy and menopause alter requirements for nutrients. At the same time, eating the right balance of foods can help limit unpleasant symptoms caused by these life changes and many other conditions. Therefore a selection of mouthwatering healthy recipes have been designed specifically to provide the range of nutrients needed by women to maintain health and vitality throughout their lives.

Women can certainly enjoy better health by following a balanced diet and creating a healthy lifestyle. Follow the guidelines in this book in order to help make this a reality for you.

learning to eat well

In order to promote optimal health, your diet needs to contain a variety of foods that will provide you with all the necessary nutrients and protective compounds. The amount of nutrients a woman needs to eat daily depends on her age, body size and composition, lifestyle factors and physiological condition (eg pregnancy or breastfeeding). These requirements are expressed as 'Dietary reference values' (previously known as Recommended Daily Amounts or RDAs). Reference Nutrient Intakes (RNIs) represent the amounts of nutrients that are needed daily in order to prevent deficiency in healthy people (the female amounts are referred to here).

All foods provide us with nutrients – carbohydrates, fats and proteins – that give our body the energy to function and remain healthy. They also contain vitamins and minerals, which are needed in smaller amounts. These do not provide energy but are still essential for good health.

CARBOHYDRATES

Carbohydrates are a group of nutrients that includes sugars, starches and fibre. When digested, carbohydrates are broken down into units of sugar that provide the body with energy. Starchy carbohydrate-rich foods include breads, rice, pasta, cereals, potatoes and pulses. Contrary to popular belief, these foods are not fattening. They are low in fat and often high in fibre and, as they're bulky, fill you up without providing too many calories. Fibre-rich varieties, like lentils, grain bread and bran cereals, release energy at a relatively slower rate, which can be useful for pregnant women, those suffering from premenstrual syndrome (PMS) and those watching their weight. At least 50 percent of daily calories should come from carbohydrates. For women consuming 2000 calories a day this means at least 265g.

FIBRE

Fibre is the indigestible part of plant foods and there are two types – insoluble and soluble. The soluble type, which is found in oats, pulses, barley and some fruit and vegetables, helps control blood sugar levels and may help to lower blood cholesterol levels. Insoluble fibre is found in grains and cereals and, when eaten regularly, helps to prevent constipation and reduces the risk of bowel cancers and haemorrhoids. The recommended intake of fibre is 18g daily. Wholegrain/wholewheat varieties of bread, rice and pasta can be much higher in fibre than 'white' varieties.

FATS

Small amounts of fat are an essential part of a healthy diet as they provide the fat-soluble vitamins A, D, E and K as well as essential fatty acids. However, most of us eat too much fat, which can lead to weight gain and an increased risk of heart disease. Fat is made up of units called fatty

PROTEIN

Protein is essential for the body's vital functions such as growth, maintenance and the repair of cells. A balanced diet containing meat, fish and pulses will contain all the protein women need. The RNI is 45g – a little extra is needed during pregnancy and breastfeeding but this isn't usually a problem as most people eat more protein than they need each day.

VITAMINS

There are two types of vitamins: fat-soluble (A, D, E and K) and water-soluble (C and B complex). With the exception of D and K, vitamins cannot be made in the body so we need to get them from our diet.

VITAMIN A

Vitamin A is needed for reproduction and development. It also helps fight infections and is vital for healthy eyes, skin and hair. There are two forms: Retinol is the ready-formed vitamin A found in foods of animal origin, such as meat and milk. Pro-vitamin A (beta-carotene and other carotenoids), is found in plant foods and can be converted into vitamin A in the body. Beta-carotene is a powerful antioxidant (see page 25) and, if eaten regularly, may protect against heart disease and cancer.

The increased amount of vitamin A needed during pregnancy and breast-feeding can easily be met by eating a varied, healthy diet. However, high intakes

acids, of which there are three main types: saturated, monounsaturated and poly-unsaturated. The fat in food contains a mixture of all three, but different foods contain different proportions of each type. For good health, no more than 35 percent of the calories that you eat daily should come from fats (of any kind). For most women this means a maximum intake of about 75g per day. Of this only 22g should be saturated (10 percent of calories). Try replacing some of the saturated fat in your diet with unsaturates. It's vital that pregnant women consume enough essential fatty acids as they cannot be made by the body. The fatty acids eicosa-pentanoic acid and docosahexanoic acid are vital for proper brain and eye development. These are best obtained by eating oily fish at least once a week.

of vitamin A may cause birth defects and supplements containing vitamin A should be avoided during pregnancy. Liver and liver products, which can contain high levels of vitamin A, should also be avoided. The RNI for vitamin A is 600mcg (750mcg in Australia), 700mcg during pregnancy and 950mcg if breastfeeding.

B VITAMINS

The B group vitamins have a variety of functions but work together to enable energy to be released from food. They are also vital for the production of blood cells as well as healthy immune and nervous systems, skin, hair and nails. Some help maintain a healthy reproductive system and play a role in early foetal development. Folic acid (folate), in particular, helps prevent babies being born with neural tube defects (eg spina bifida) and women may be advised to take a supplement of 400mcg a day from the time they start trying to conceive until the 12th week of pregnancy. The RNI for non-pregnant women is 200mcg. Useful sources are liver, leafy vegetables, pulses, nuts, wholemeal bread and oranges. Vitamin B6 (pyridoxine) has a RNI of 1.2mg a day and may help sufferers of PMS. But too much may cause nerve damage so the maximum dose is 10mg.

VITAMIN C

Vitamin C helps strengthen blood vessels and is essential for healthy skin, bones and teeth. It also promotes healing and keeps ligaments, tendons and gums healthy. As a powerful antioxidant it may also protect against cancers and heart disease. It also increases the absorption of iron from plant foods. The RNI for vitamin C is 40mg a day for adult women, 50mg during pregnancy and 70mg during breastfeeding. Good sources include most fruit and vegetables.

VITAMIN D

Vitamin D is essential for the absorption of calcium from foods. Although we get some vitamin D from our diet, we mainly manufacture it in our skin when it is exposed to sunlight. If you cover up your skin outdoors for cultural reasons and/or follow a strict vegetarian diet you may not be getting sufficient vitamin D.

Vitamin D supplements may be recommended for pregnant and breast-feeding women as well as older women who are housebound or have a restricted diet. There is no RNI, but pregnant and breastfeeding women should try to get 10mcg daily from their diet.

VITAMIN E

Vitamin E is a powerful antioxidant that may help protect against cancer and heart disease. It is also essential for healthy skin. It may enhance the immune system and protect against environmental toxins and some claim it helps slow down the ageing process. Few foods are rich in vitamin E (wheatgerm, nuts, leafy green vegetables are), but it can be stored in the body so deficiency is rare. There is no RNI but a safe intake is more than 3mg.

MINERALS

Minerals are vital to many body processes and, as they cannot be made by the body, they have to be supplied by our food. Some important minerals for women include:

CALCIUM

This is essential for healthy bones and teeth. It is important for women to ensure an adequate calcium intake throughout life to reduce the risk of osteoporosis (see page 24). Calcium also helps regulate nerve and muscle function and is necessary for blood clotting as well as controlling blood pressure. The RNI for calcium is 700mg a day. This is not raised during pregnancy as the increased need for calcium is thought to be entirely met by an increased efficiency in absorption. An extra 550mg a day, however, is recommended during breastfeeding.

Women who do not regularly eat dairy products need to ensure that their diet contains sufficient calcium-rich foods (such as canned fish, nuts and seeds, dried fruit, pulses, calcium fortified soy products).

IRON

Because women lose blood during their menstrual cycle they also lose iron, so it's important that their diet contains iron-rich foods. Good sources include red meat liver, fish, sardines, mussesls, fortified breakfast cereals, green leafy vegetables, tofu and nuts. Iron from non-meat sources is less easily absorbed by the body but vitamin C can help. The RNI for iron is 14.8mg and this drops to 8.7mg at menopause. An increased absorption of iron is thought to meet the extra requirements during pregnancy, but supplements may be needed if a women starts pregnancy with low iron stores.

MAGNESIUM

Magnesium is needed for our muscles to function normally and may help ease PMS and menstrual cramps in some women. It may also be beneficial in preventing heart disease and preserving bone strength in post-menopausal women. Good sources are wholegrains, nuts, legumes, dark green leafy vegetables and shellfish. RNI is 270mg a day – 320mg when breastfeeding.

ZINC

This mineral is essential for normal growth and development. It's also needed for the development of the reproductive organs, healthy teeth, bones, skin, nails and eyes. Zinc is also needed for immunity and healing. The RNI for zinc is 7mg a day and 9.5–13mg if breastfeeding. Good sources include seafood, meat, dairy products and some green leafy vegetables and cereals.

HEALTHY EATING PLAN

FOOD GROUP	EXAMPLE FOODS	RECOMMENDATIONS
BREADS, CEREALS AND POTATOES	Breads, rice, maize, millet, breakfast cereals, oats, pasta, noodles, potatoes	Have at least six servings a day. A serving is: 1 slice of bread, ½ bagel, 1 bowl cereal, 30g (2 tbsp) cooked rice, 45g (3 tbsp) cooked pasta or noodles
FRUIT AND VEGETABLES	Fresh, frozen and canned fruit and vegetables and dried fruit. A glass of fruit juice can also contribute	Eat at least five portions a day. A portion is: 30g (2 tbsp) cooked vegetables or fruit, a side salad, 1 medium fruit, 1 glass fruit juice, 15g (1 tbsp) dried fruit
MILK AND DAIRY PRODUCTS	Milk, cheese, yoghurt and fromage frais, but not butter, eggs and cream	Eat two to three servings of these foods a day and choose lower fat alternatives where possible. One serving is: 200ml (6½ fl oz) milk, 1 small pot yoghurt, 25g (1oz) cheese, 100g (3½oz) cottage cheese
MEAT, FISH AND ALTERNATIVES	Meat, poultry, fish, eggs, nuts, textured vegetable protein, tofu, beans and pulses	Eat two to three servings of these foods a day and try to remove any excess fat. One serving is: 50–75mg (2–3oz) meat, 100g (3½oz) fish, 1–2 eggs, 45–60g (3–4 tbsp) cooked pulses, 50g (2oz) nuts
WATER	Tap, bottled (carbonated or still)	Drink eight to ten glasses of fluids a day as your body constantly loses water

foods to eat in moderation

There is no such thing as an unhealthy 'food', just an unhealthy 'diet'. Therefore there's no need to totally ban any foods from a healthy diet. However, certain foods and drinks should be consumed in moderation to protect your well-being.

FATTY, SUGARY FOODS

Fatty foods include fats such as butter, oil, margarine and salad dressings (eg mayonnaise, vinaigrette) as well as pastries, pies, biscuits, cakes, chocolate, confectionery, ice cream and crisps. Although small amounts of fat are essential most of us eat too much, which puts us at increased risk of heart disease and weight gain. These foods should be eaten sparingly so, whenever possible, choose low-fat alternatives. Although sugar intake itself is not associated with increased risk of disease (other than tooth decay), sugary foods and drinks are often high in calories but contain few nutrients. Therefore, consuming large amounts may contribute towards weight gain.

SALT

Salt (sodium chloride) in very small amounts is a vital constituent of our diet. Eating too much salt can increase the amount of fluid that you retain in your body. This raises blood pressure, which can lead to stroke or heart attack. It may also contribute to premenstrual bloating. The RNI is about 4g per day. Although it's important to cut down on the amount of salt you add to cooking or at the table, most of the salt we eat (about 70 percent) comes from processed foods including bread and cereals. Although food labels usually give values for sodium (or 'Na') not salt, you can work out the salt content by multiplying the sodium value by 2.5.

ALCOHOL

In moderation, alcohol can be an enjoyable part of life and does not appear to increase the risk of health problems in most people. However, excessive drinking can deplete the body of vitamins and increase the risk of developing high blood pressure, osteoporosis, heart disease, obesity and cancer. It is recommended that women have a maximum of two to three units of alcohol a day and always have some alcohol-free days each week. One unit of alcohol refers to 12fl oz (½ pint) of normal strength lager, bitter or cider, a small glass of wine or one pub measure of a spirit.

CAFFEINE

Caffeine-containing drinks include coffee, tea and cola. Caffeine acts as a stimulant and in some individuals it produces an increased heart rate and restlessness. Although not directly linked with ill health, it's best to limit your intake of caffeinated drinks to four or five a day, especially during pregnancy.

energy requirements

All the energy we need comes from food. The carbohydrate, protein, fat and alcohol in foods and drinks can all be burned up by the body to provide us with energy (calories). Fat provides more than twice as much energy per gram as carbohydrate, while alcohol contains *nearly* twice as much. So it's easy to consume too much energy on a high fat diet or with heavy drinking. If energy intake exceeds the amount of energy we burn up, it is stored as fat and leads to weight gain. Being a healthy weight is an important part of maintaining optimum health.

HOW MUCH ENERGY?

Basal metabolic rate (BMR) is the rate at which your body uses energy to maintain the basic functions that keep it alive, such as keeping the heart beating and the kidneys working. Use the equation in the table below that is relevant to your age and insert your weight in kilograms to find out what your personal BMR rating is.

The amount of energy needed each day depends on age, body size, physiological status and activity level. The greater the body size and activity level, the higher the energy requirements. Energy needs are therefore determined by using the BMR as well as physical activity level. To calculate your daily energy requirement in kilocalories multiply your BMR value with the value that best matches your average activity level (see box below).

To give you an example: a 36-year-old woman who weighs 72 kg, works in an office and swims twice a week would have the following calorie requirement:
$(8.3 \times 72) + 846 = 1444 \times 1.4 = 2022$ calories per day. (The average woman aged 19 to 50 years needs 2000 calories daily.)

APPROXIMATE BMR VALUES

AGE	BMR
18–29 years	$14.8 \times kg + 487$
30–59 years	$8.3 \times kg + 846$
over 60 years	$(0.038 \times kg + 2.755) \times 239$

Source: Department of Health COMA report Dietary Reference Values for Foods Energy and Nutrients for the UK (1991)

ADULT WOMEN'S ACTIVITY LEVELS

	NON-WORK ACTIVITY	WORK ACTIVITY	
	Light	Moderate	Moderate/Heavy
Non-active	1.4*	1.5	1.5
Moderately active	1.5	1.6	1.6
Very active	1.6	1.7	1.7

* An activity level of 1.4 is applicable to most people – it represents little activity at work (eg office work) or in leisure time

ARE YOU OVERWEIGHT?

Obesity is one of the fastest growing health problems in the modern world. Latest estimates show that over half of women are overweight and 20 percent are obese. Obesity is associated with increased risk of heart disease, stroke, some cancers, diabetes, high blood pressure, infertility, osteoarthritis and back problems. It can also cause depression and low self-esteem. There is no single ideal weight at which you will be 'healthy', but there is a range of weights based on your height that you should aim to fall between for good health. Calculating your body mass index (BMI) is a good way to see if you are maintaining a healthy weight.

BMI = weight (kg) / height^2 (m^2). For example, a 72kg woman, who is 1.63m tall, would have a BMI of $72/(1.63)^2 = 27$ (now see box, above right).

APPLES AND PEARS

There is some evidence that the distribution of fat in your body may be important with respect to disease risk. If you carry a lot of fat around your middle (apple shaped), rather than round your hips and lower limbs (pear shaped), you may be at increased risk of heart disease and diabetes. Distribution of fat is sometimes measured by a waist/hip ratio. A high waist/hip ratio may indicate an increased risk of heart disease due to detrimental changes in metabolism.

BMI DEFINITIONS	
less than 18	Underweight
18–20	A healthy weight but do not lose any more
20–25	A healthy weight
25–30	Overweight
30–40	Obese
over 40	Very obese

LOSING WEIGHT

Many factors contribute to obesity but the one indisputable fact is that energy (calorie) intake must exceed energy expenditure for weight gain to occur.

For an average women who maintains her weight on 2000 calories, eating 1500 calories a day would result in a weight loss of about 450g (1lb) per week. This can be done easily by replacing some of the fat in a diet with starchy, fibre-rich foods. Eating too few calories in order to lose weight quickly can be damaging to your health. Temporarily lowering your metabolic rate can also contribute to subsequent weight gain and 'yo yo' dieting. Following the latest diet crazes may result in short term weight loss but rarely helps maintain a healthy weight. Slavishly counting calories and weighing yourself is not the solution either. Rather, be more physically active, enjoy your food and encourage the whole family to eat healthily (see page 12).

changing needs

As a woman develops and ages her nutritional needs alter. Consequently dietary changes will also be needed to ensure optimal health.

MENSTRUATION

The average age that girls start menstruating is 13 years. At this time, the need for dietary iron increases sharply. This extra iron is needed to replace what is lost from the body during menstruation. Additional iron is also needed during the rapid growth spurt that occurs during adolescence. Fortunately, during these times the body has the capacity to increase the amount of iron absorbed from the diet. However, most of the iron we consume is not absorbed (typically only 10 percent is), so women must make a conscious effort to make iron-rich foods such as lean meat and eggs a regular part of their diet. Unfortunately, nutrition surveys show that approximately one third of women aged between 16 and 64 years consume less than the RNI amount for iron (14.9 mg daily) and iron deficiency anaemia is a problem for women of all age groups.

IRON DEFICIENCY ANAEMIA

Iron deficiency is prevalent among adolescent girls and women in their reproductive years, especially those with very heavy periods. It can eventually lead to anaemia (the point at which the body's iron stores are totally exhausted).

Haemoglobin production falls as iron deficiency progresses, which results in a reduced supply of oxygen to the body's tissues. Consequently, the symptoms of anaemia include tiredness, irritability, muscle weakness, mental confusion, numbness and tingling of the feet or legs, breathlessness, paleness and heart palpitations, a decreased tolerance to cold, depression, impaired physical and mental performance and a reduced ability to recover from exercise. If you think that you may be iron deficient, it's important that you visit your doctor. Don't self-diagnose and start taking iron tablets, because this could cause other problems.

Iron deficiency can be avoided by making sure you that you regularly consume iron-rich foods (see page 11). But if you are iron deficient, try to eat lean meat or fish three or four times a week to help boost your iron stores. Vitamin C can increase the amount of iron absorbed from non-meat sources, so add vitamin C-rich foods such as citrus fruits and red peppers to your meals. This is especially important for vegetarians as it's much harder for them to eat enough iron. Very high intakes of fibre can interfere with iron absorption so avoid consuming lots of bran or bran-based cereals if your diet is lacking in iron and look for iron-enriched breakfast cereals. Similarly, red wine and tannin in tea can reduce iron absorption, so avoid consuming these with your meals.

PREMENSTRUAL SYNDROME (PMS)
Many women are only too familiar with the emotional and physical rollercoaster they experience in the week or two leading up to their menstrual period. There are hundreds of different symptoms but the most common are mood swings, anxiety, depression, irritability, a lack of energy, food cravings, breast pain and tenderness, bloating, headache and back pain.

Why some women suffer from PMS and others don't is still a mystery. PMS symptoms are associated with changing hormonal patterns due to the menstrual cycle, and usually begin during ovulation and cease with menstruation. At the start of a woman's menstrual cycle, the level of the hormone oestrogen increases while the level of progesterone is low. After ovulation, the level of oestrogen decreases while the level of progesterone increases.

Some research studies have found that women who regularly experience PMS have an excess of oestrogen in the second half of the menstrual cycle following ovulation. Too much oestrogen combined with too little progesterone may be connected with changes in the balance of brain chemicals that control mood and pain. These imbalances may also be linked to increased levels of the hormone prolactin, which can increase breast tenderness. Another theory is that in other women low levels of the brain chemicals dopamine and serotonin cause PMS symptoms. Neither of these theories have been clinically proven, but many practitioners agree that symptoms can be eased with diet and lifestyle changes.

WHAT ABOUT SUPPLEMENTS?
Some experts advise taking supplements to relieve PMS. There is little scientific evidence that they work, but some women find them helpful.

* **Evening primrose oil** This oil contains the essential fatty acid gamma linoleic acid (GLA), which the body converts into the hormone-like compounds prostaglandins. These reduce the sensitivity of various tissues to female hormones and some women find that GLA is helpful for reducing breast tenderness.

* **Fish oil** These capsules contain omega-3 essential fatty acids and have been shown to help reduce the pain of cramps.

This is probably because omega-3 fats reduce the production of the inflammatory agent prostaglandin E and painful cramps are linked to its overproduction. Doses of more than 1 gram of omega-3 fatty acids should be avoided by people with asthma, diabetes or blood-clotting disorders and those taking blood-thinning medications.

* **Magnesium** Some women have found that extra magnesium helps to ease the symptoms of PMS and menstrual cramps.

THINGS TO HELP RELIEVE PMS

* Reduce your fat intake. Eat oily fish at least three to four times a week as omega-3 fatty acids help alleviate symptoms and cramp.

* Increase your fruit and vegetable intake and the consumption of wholegrain cereals.

* Eat less salt and salty foods as they can contribute to water retention and bloating.

* Cut back on caffeine-containing drinks as some studies suggest they exacerbate breast tenderness and other PMS symptoms.

* Avoid alcohol as it exaggerates mood swings and behaviour changes.

* Regular exercise may help release fluids that cause bloating and breast tenderness, as well as alleviate feelings of depression.

* Try to increase your intake of nutritious carbohydrate-rich foods as they may increase the levels of circulating serotonin – thought to be deficient in some PMS sufferers.

* Limit your intake of sugary foods to help reduce dizziness, irritability and shakiness.

---

* **St John's Wort** This is sometimes recommended if the primary PMS symptom is depression or anxiety. It should not be consumed by those taking antidepressant medications.

* **Vitamin B6** Supplements for this vitamin have long been recommended for the treatment of PMS, although there is little evidence that they really help. In fact, regularly taking high doses (above 50mg/day) may cause nerve damage – the Department of Health now recommends that the maximum daily intake of vitamin B6 should not be more than 10mg.

FERTILITY AND CONCEPTION

Maintaining a healthy weight and eating a healthy balanced diet at least several months before you try to conceive gives you the best possible chance of becoming pregnant. Women who are very thin may experience difficulties in conceiving as hormone imbalances may prevent ovulation and conception. At the other extreme, obesity is also associated with fertility problems and birth defects. Therefore, it's important to achieve a healthy weight (see page 15) before you try to conceive. Dieting immediately prior to conception may result in nutritional deficiencies that could adversely affect a foetus. If you are trying to conceive you should:

* See your doctor to find out if you should take a daily folic acid supplement (400mcg per day) from the time you start trying to

changes taking place in her own body and provide for the development of her baby. Focusing on eating more nutrients per mouthful is an important strategy when pregnant. Generally, a well-balanced diet will provide all the necessary nutrients.

The best advice is to eat according to your appetite during pregnancy. There's certainly no need to 'eat for two' and your calorie requirement does not increase in the first six months of pregnancy. An additional 200–300 kilocalories a day is recommended in the last 3 months of pregnancy, but may not be necessary if physical activity levels have fallen greatly. Excessive weight gain during pregnancy should be avoided as it can cause complications during the birth and can be difficult to lose afterwards.

conceive until the 12th week of pregnancy. Folic acid is known to reduce the risk of babies being born with neural tube defects such as spina bifida.

* Eat plenty of foods rich in folic acid such as fortified breakfast cereal, leafy green vegetables and oranges.
* Stop smoking, avoid alcohol and limit tea and coffee to four cups a day.
* Limit your intake of dietary fat, particularly saturated fats, but ensure that you have an adequate intake of healthy fats from foods like sardines, tuna and soy products.
* Regularly eat iron-rich foods such as lean meat, fish, eggs and nuts.

PREGNANCY

During pregnancy, a woman's diet needs to provide all the nutrients necessary to maintain her own health, fuel the physical

EXTRA NUTRIENT REQUIREMENTS

A woman's protein requirement increases by 10 grams per day throughout pregnancy to provide for the extra blood supply and tissues and also for the growth of the baby. Typically, non-pregnant women eat more protein than they require on a daily basis, so it's not too difficult to reach this goal.

Iron needs are high during pregnancy and iron deficiency is a common problem, since many women start their pregnancy with relatively low iron stores. So try to include some foods containing easily absorbed iron in your diet every day (eg fish, lean meat and chicken). If you are vegetarian, include pulses or eggs in your diet and always have some vitamin C-rich foods in your meal to help to increase iron absorption from non-meat sources.

The need for extra calcium during pregnancy is thought to be met entirely by the increased ability to absorb calcium. However, many women regularly eat less than the RNI amount (700 mg daily), so be conscientious about your calcium intake.

There is an increased requirement for some vitamins during pregnancy. For example, folic acid can help prevent birth defects and in addition to the supplement recommended pre-conceptually, pregnant women should aim to eat as many folate-rich foods as possible. Vitamin B12 is needed to regenerate the active forms of folate in the body, so an adequate intake of B12 before and during pregnancy is also essential. Vitamin A can be absorbed from a varied diet. High intakes of this vitamin may cause birth defects so do not take supplements and also avoid liver and liver products (eg liverwurst, pâté) as they can contain high doses of vitamin A.

* **Vitamin C** The RNI for vitamin C is increased for pregnant women from 40 to 50 mg/day.

* **Vitamin D** This vitamin enables your body to absorb more of the calcium from your food. Normally the vitamin D we synthesize in our skin is enough, but pregnant women are advised to get at least 10mcg vitamin D from their diet.

POST-PREGNANCY/BREASTFEEDING

Eating a balanced diet is the best way to shed excess pounds after you've given birth. Do not be tempted to crash diet as this can compromise your health and ability to breastfeed. Having a new baby can be very tiring and you will need to eat healthily to maintain your energy levels and replenish your body's nutrient stores. The energy needed to produce breast milk will naturally come from the fat stores you laid down during pregnancy, so breastfeeding itself is helpful for shedding some of the weight you will have gained. Breastfeeding has a number of benefits for both you and your baby. It helps strengthen the bond between you, provides your baby with antibodies and nutrients and helps your uterus to contract back to normal.

It is estimated that women need an extra 500 kilocalories per day when breastfeeding. The daily requirements for many vitamins and minerals are also increased, in particular the B-group vitamins (including folate and B12), vitamins A, C, D, calcium and phosphorus. 'Dieting' during breastfeeding is therefore not a good idea but neither should you use breastfeeding as an excuse to eat too many fatty or sugary foods. As with pregnancy, you need more nutrients per mouthful when breastfeeding. Make sure you:

* Drink plenty of fluids, especially in hot weather. Breastfeeding increases your

daily fluid needs by at least one litre (1¾ pints). Take a water bottle with you when going out and have an extra glass of water with every meal and when breastfeeding. Consuming extra milk will help you meet your increased needs for fluid and calcium.

* Eat well at meals times and base your main meals on starchy foods (bread, pasta, rice, and potatoes) as well as fresh fruit and vegetables.

* Eat healthy snacks between meals (eg fresh fruit, a handful of nuts and seeds, low-fat yoghurt).

* Depending on your health status and appetite, you may be advised to take a vitamin and/or mineral supplement. Check with your doctor to confirm that they are safe for you.

COPING WITH MENOPAUSE

Menopause is a natural and important stage in a woman's life and generally occurs between the ages of 45 and 55 years, when the ovaries gradually stop producing eggs and the menstrual cycle becomes irregular and finally ceases. As the ovaries stop producing the hormones oestrogen and progesterone, menopausal symptoms such as hot flushes, night sweats, mood swings and depression can increase. Some women find these unbearable while others have few problems at all. This difference is probably due to a combination of diet, lifestyle and genetic factors. Smoking or excessive alcohol consumption

(more than ten drinks a week) is associated with an earlier and more severe menopause. Therefore modifications to your diet can help. Some plant foods, for example, contain compounds called phytoestrogens that may offer a number of health benefits (see box, below).

Before menopause, female hormones help protect women from heart disease and osteoporosis. Unfortunately, at the onset of menopause this protection is lost and women are at increased risk of both diseases. While diet can be used to alleviate symptoms, many women try

PHYTOESTROGENS

Phytoestrogens ('phyto' means plant) are compounds found in some plants that can either mimic the effects of the hormone oestrogen in the body or block its effects (anti-oestrogens). Compounds called isoflavones are among the most powerful of the phytoestrogens and occur in significant amounts in legumes, particularly soya beans. It is widely promoted that phytoestrogens alleviate menopausal symptoms in women and prevent osteoporosis and heart disease, but further scientific research is needed to establish if this is true. To be well absorbed by the body isoflavones must be broken down by bacteria in the large intestine. Eating a low-fat diet based on plant foods can promote a good balance of gut bacteria, which may encourage isoflavone absorption.

hormone replacement therapy (HRT), as it can relieve symptoms such as hot flushes and night sweats and can help reduce risk of osteoporosis and heart disease if taken for at least five years. However, speak to your doctor about this treatment as HRT is not suitable for every woman.

The body's need for iron falls at menopause because you are no longer losing blood. But it's essential to ensure you're getting enough calcium, vitamin D and phosphorous to help slow down the loss of bone mass that occurs with ageing. So ensure you are eating plenty of foods such as nuts, seeds and canned fish.

It's not uncommon for women to gain weight after the menopause, which can increase blood cholesterol and the risk of heart disease. Maintaining physical activity, eating a balanced diet and limiting alcohol intake can help prevent weight gain.

COMBATING AGEING

You can't stop the clock from ticking, but you can help delay the signs of ageing by maintaining a healthy diet and lifestyle. This will provide you with all the energy, vitamins, minerals and phytochemicals you need to boost your immune system and help prevent degenerative conditions.

SKIN, NAILS AND HAIR

Problems with skin, hair and nails can indicate an underlying illness, nutrient deficiency or medical condition. Eating the right balance of nutrients and de-stressing are the best ways of keeping your skin, hair and nails looking great. You are what you eat so you can't cut corners in your eating habits and not expect it to show!

* **Youthful skin** Our skin is made up of millions of living cells that depend on a regular supply of nutrients and oxygen to keep working effectively. A decline in the quality of your diet or in your health will quickly start to show in your skin, because skin cells have a very short life span. Eating a balanced diet rich in fruit and vegetables and taking time to exercise will be more effective at helping you prevent skin problems and maintain youthful skin than depending on creams and supplements as it's not just enough to treat the surface – you have to nourish your whole body.

The antioxidant nutrients vitamins C and E, beta-carotene and selenium may help protect the skin from damage caused by free radicals. Antioxidants are now being added to face creams and lotions but, with the exception of vitamin E, these are not absorbed well through the skin. So the consumption of anti-oxidant-rich foods, such as citrus fruits and carrots, is important. Vitamin C is vital for a healthy skin colour, C and E aid wound healing and vitamin A is essential for maintaining moist skin. Fish oils, found in salmon, tuna etc, can help dry skin and eczema while zinc is needed to promote tissue repair and improved immunity. Zinc is sometimes used to treat acne and may be useful for alleviating inflammatory skin problems so be sure to eat plenty of zinc-rich seafood, lean meat and dairy products.

* **Nurtured nails** Nails are composed mainly of a fibrous protein called keratin. Healthy nails are strong, smooth and pink and nutrition plays a key role in nail growth and appearance. Low intakes of B vitamins and selenium can produce ridges in nails, whereas thin, spoon-shaped nails can indicate an iron deficiency. Many people think that calcium-rich foods will make their nails stronger. In fact, the small white flecks on nails often thought to be caused by calcium deficiency are more likely to be caused by a knock or lack of zinc. Low intakes of zinc may also cause brittle nails, prone to infection. Protein, B vitamins, vitamins A, C and E, biotin and copper have a synergistic effect so help the body to build keratin and other compounds that keep nails healthy.

TIPS FOR HEALTHY SKIN, NAILS, HAIR

* Drink plenty of water (8–10 glasses a day).
* Avoid overexposure to the sun.
* Avoid consuming too much alcohol or caffeine-containing drinks.
* Don't smoke.
* Eat a low-fat diet based on fresh fruit and vegetables (at least five portions daily), wholegrain cereal products and pulses.
* Make sure you get regular exercise.

---

* **Healthy hair** Stress, poor diet and hormonal changes can result in hair loss and problems. Hair is a non-living tissue made up mainly of keratin that requires a plentiful supply of nutrient-rich blood. Lack of vitamin A may lead to a flaky scalp but too much may lead to hair loss.

Zinc is needed for healthy skin, hair and nails so may aid brittle and thinning hair, while selenium encourages healthy hair growth. Selenium or omega-3 fatty acids (oily fish is the best source) may also help prevent a dry, flaking scalp. Hair follicles also need essential amino acids found in quality protein foods such as lean meat and eggs. People who suffer from high levels of stress may need higher amounts of B vitamins, which are also essential for healthy hair and are found in foods such as meat, chicken, fish, cereals and nuts.

A WORD ABOUT DETOX DIETS

It has become very fashionable to follow so-called 'detox' diets that claim to flush out all the toxins from your body. These diets typically require fasting or severely limiting food intake. While a 24-hour fast won't harm a healthy person, it won't flush the toxins out of your body any more effectively than regularly drinking water. In fact, a healthy person's lungs, skin, liver and kidneys are naturally 'detoxifying' 24 hours a day. There is little evidence that 'detoxing' works so it should never be a substitute for a healthy diet and lifestyle.

diseases common in women

Ill health does not have to be an inevitable part of ageing! Diet plays a huge role in the development of some of the diseases that are common in women such as cancer, heart disease and osteoporosis. Eating a diet based on The Healthy Eating Plan on page 12 can help prevent these degenerative diseases and help you enjoy good health as you age.

OSTEOPOROSIS

The term osteoporosis literally means porous bones. Bones are made out of a thick outer shell and a strong inner mesh that looks like honeycomb with blood vessels and bone marrow in the holes between bone. Osteoporosis occurs when these holes become bigger, making the bone weak and thin.

Throughout life bone is changing as old or damaged bone is replaced or repaired. Up until about the age of 35 years, the balance between bone break-down and formation generally remains stable. After this age we start to lose bone as a natural part of ageing. Unfortunately, this loss of bone speeds up for women after the menopause, which increases the risk of osteoporosis and bone fracture.

HOW DIET CAN HELP

To achieve and maintain healthy bones you need to eat a balanced diet that contains plenty of calcium. Most of the calcium in the body is stored in bone and it is this that helps maintain bone strength and rigidity. If you have a low calcium intake, calcium will be released from your bones in order to increase the level in your blood.

To avoid osteoporosis, it is therefore important to eat plenty of dairy products or calcium-enriched alternatives such as soya milk and tofu. You should also not smoke, avoid adding salt to your meals and not consume too much alcohol, caffeine and protein (the more protein you eat the more calcium you excrete). You should also eat plenty of fresh vegetables and fruit (antioxidants help protect the bones), exercise regularly and maintain a healthy weight.

HEART DISEASE

Many people think that heart disease is a man's disease. However, heart disease is still the main cause of death in women.

The term cardiovascular disease is used to describe coronary heart disease (CHD) and stroke. CHD appears as angina or a heart attack, whereas strokes are caused by clots in the blood vessels that block the supply of blood to the brain. There are two main changes that lead to cardiovascular disease. The first is hardening of the arteries (atherosclerosis) where the lining of the arteries becomes thicker until there's only a very small hole through which blood can flow. Secondly, when the thickened part of the artery wall becomes unstable and splits, blood clumps together to seal the split by forming a thrombus (or blood clot). This process is called thrombosis and may result in partial or total blocking of the flow of blood to the heart or brain to cause a heart attack or stroke.

There is no single cause of heart disease. Some of the factors that contribute to it are out of our control (eg genetics), but it is possible to reduce risk by controlling factors influenced by diet and lifestyle.

HOW DIET CAN HELP
Diet can affect blood pressure, blood cholesterol levels and obesity. Women tend to have a lower blood pressure than men, but for both sexes it rises markedly with age. A diet that is low in salt and rich in calcium and essential fatty acids, however, may help to lower raised blood pressure.

A certain amount of cholesterol is needed for good health but many people have too much in their bloodstream, which increases the risk of stroke and heart disease. Reducing your fat intake and replacing saturated fat with poly-unsaturated and monounsaturated fats can help. Other factors include smoking, low physical activity levels and stress.

CANCER
It has been estimated that between 30 and 40 percent of cancers could be prevented by a healthy diet and lifestyle. The development of cancer is a complex biological process involving hormones, inherited genetic traits and environmental factors. Diet and lifestyle are, however, also known to have a significant influence on its development.

HOW DIET CAN HELP
By eating at least five varied portions of fruit and vegetables every day you can lower the risk of developing cancer. Also make starchy foods the main part of your meals and avoid processed, fatty foods. There is evidence that phytoestrogens found in plant foods (see also page 21) may mimic the effect of oestrogen and help reduce the risk of hormone-dependent cancers like breast cancer. You should also limit alcohol and not smoke.

WHAT ARE ANTIOXIDANTS?
Antioxidants are powerful protective substances that are able to mop up potentially harmful molecules in the body called free radicals. These molecules are produced during normal bodily processes, but their production may be increased by external factors such as smoking, pollution and stress. If too many free radicals are left to roam around the body they may contribute to the development of heart disease, osteoporosis and cancer. The principal antioxidant nutrients are selenium, vitamins C, E and carotenes. Eating plenty of fruit and vegetables is the best way to ensure you are getting a good supply of antioxidants and other phytochemicals.

---

breads, cereals and potatoes

At least 50 percent of our daily calorie intake should come from starchy carbohydrates which are found in foods such as breads, cereals, pasta, rice, couscous and potatoes.

* **Bread** is generally low in fat and high in starchy carbohydrate. White bread is fortified with calcium, niacin, iron and thiamin, whereas wholemeal bread is richer in fibre, iron, zinc and B vitamins and also contains some vitamin E. Choosing grainy bread is a good way to boost both your fibre and nutrient intake. Wholewheat bread (which contains the outer bran and inner germ) also has within it phytochemicals called lignans, which may help fight disease.

* **Cereals** – Eating a fibre-rich whole-grain breakfast cereal is a great way to start the day as it provides a low-fat source of slowly released energy. Cereals are also often fortified with vitamins and minerals – check the ingredient panel. Oats are rich in soluble fibre, which helps to slow down the rate of digestion ensuring a slow, steady release of glucose energy into the bloodstream and helps prolong the feeling of fullness.

* **Potatoes** are not fattening – it's the fat that they are cooked or served with (eg butter, cheese, cream) that can be a problem. They contain less than 1 percent fat and, when eaten with their skins, are good sources of fibre, potassium and the antioxidant vitamin C. Some vitamin C is lost during cooking, but microwaving or steaming potatoes is a good way to preserve more of their vitamin C content. Sweet potatoes are a delicious alternative and are good sources of the antioxidants beta-carotene and vitamin C.

* **Pasta and rice** – Pasta is an excellent low-fat source of slowly released energy. As with any grain, the more refined it is the less nutrients there are so wholewheat varieties are best. Many of the nutrients in rice are contained in the bran and germ (eg B vitamins essential for fertility and healthy complexion). However, the phytic acid present in brown rice can reduce the absorption of calcium and iron – two essential nutrients for women. The starch in rice, particularly brown rice is digested slowly providing a steady release of glucose into the body. This is essential for diabetics, but may also be an important way to help reduce the symptoms of PMS.

FOCUS ON FIBRE

* If you are not used to eating a high fibre diet always increase your fibre intake slowly and drink plenty of fluids to avoid constipation. Choosing wholewheat pasta, bread and cereals as well as wholegrain rice and eating potatoes with their skins will significantly increase your fibre intake.

sweet potatoes

white rice

egg noodles

couscous

bulgar wheat

oats

wholemeal bread

ciabatta bread

breakfast cereal

pulses, nuts and seeds

As well as helping to reduce saturated fat and increase fibre, including plenty of these foods in your diet greatly increases your intake of antioxidant nutrients.

* **Pulses** – This group includes lentils, beans and peas, which are readily available dried or canned (ready-to-eat). Being low in fat and high in protein and fibre these foods are great replacements for meat as they help to lower saturated fat intake, although they do contain less iron and zinc. The starch in pulses is slowly absorbed, so they can help to maintain a stable blood sugar level – useful for alleviating fatigue and premenstrual symptoms. Most pulses also contain iron, potassium, phosphorus, magnesium, manganese and B vitamins (except B12). Soya beans and their products (tofu, tempeh and soya milk) are rich in phytoestrogens called isoflavones, which have antioxidant effects. Chickpeas, soya beans and lentils contain phytochemicals called saponins, which can enhance the removal of cholesterol from the body.

* **Nuts** generally contain 50 percent fat (except chestnuts, which have about 3 percent) but it's mostly unsaturated fat. As they are also high in calories, eating large quantities of nuts may contribute to weight gain. However, they are nutritious so are a useful snack or salad topping. Nuts are also a good source of protein for vegetarians and provide the antioxidants vitamin E and selenium, as well as B vitamins, iron and essential fatty acids. Brazil nuts are a very rich source of selenium, which is a powerful antioxidant.

* **Seeds** are little nuggets of nutrition containing unsaturated fat, fibre, some B vitamins, vitamin E and phytochemicals. Like nuts, eating them as a snack is a great way to boost your nutrient intake. Pumpkin and sunflower seeds are good sources of zinc and phytochemicals, manganese, copper, phosphorous, magnesium and folate. Linseed is a rich source of omega-3 fat and phyto-chemicals called lignans that may help reduce the risk of cancer. Some studies also suggest that the regular consumption of linseeds may help to alleviate meno-pausal symptoms as well as improve inflammatory conditions.

FOCUS ON SOYA BEANS

* Unlike other beans, soya beans are a complete source of protein. They are also higher in fat, but the majority is unsaturated and includes essential omega-3 fats. Compared to animal protein, it is thought that soya protein reduces the amount of calcium lost in urine, which may be important in post-menopausal women who have increased loss of bone minerals.

black eye beans

chestnuts

chickpeas

pumpkin seeds

nut butter

brazil nuts

soya beans

tofu

mung beans

fats and oils

We all need some fat in our diet as it supplies essential acids and vitamins A, D, E and K. However, most of us eat far too much fat, which can cause health and weight problems.

* **Butter and other solid fats** – In general, the harder the fat, the more saturated it is. Animal fats such as lard, butter and dripping are high in saturated fat and trans fatty acids. A high intake of these fats is associated with raised blood cholesterol levels and a greater risk of heart disease. However, butter is a source of vitamins A, D and E and in small quantities can be part of a healthy diet. Solid vegetable fats (eg copha) are usually made from palm oil and coconut oil and are high in saturated fatty acids.

* **Margarines** – All fats, including margarines, are a concentrated source of calories, which means that even moderate amounts can contribute towards weight gain. Margarines can be divided into hard, soft and soft margarines that are 'high in polyunsaturates'. Hard and soft varieties contain a relatively high proportion of saturated fat and trans fatty acids (usually less than butter), but they have the same total fat and calorie content as butter. Those labelled 'high in polyunsaturates' contain much less saturated fat but the same total fat and calories. Soft margarines high in monounsaturates such as olive oil are now available, as are spreading fats enriched with plant sterols. It is claimed that these plant sterols help reduce raised cholesterol levels, but they are unlikely to have any effect unless eaten as part of a healthy low-fat diet. Low-fat spreads contain half the fat of butter or margarine.

* **Speciality oils** – include walnut, hazelnut, sesame and almond, which are good sources of essential fatty acids and are low in saturates. They are strongly flavoured and only needed in small amounts. Linseed oil in particular, is a good source of omega-3 fatty acids.

FOCUS ON MONOUNSATURATES

* Monounsaturated fatty acids can be made by the body and are, therefore, not considered 'essential'. Many different foods contain some monounsaturates (including animal fats), but olive oil contains approximately 76 percent monounsaturated fat. The popularity of olive oil as a 'health' food stems from that fact that it contains monounsaturates and antioxidants. When monounsaturates are used to replace saturated fat in the diet, levels of 'bad' LDL (low-density lipoprotein) cholesterol can be reduced without lowering the levels of so-called 'good' HDL (high-density lipoprotein) cholesterol levels. However, olive oil still contains the same amount of fat and calories as other fats and too much can contribute to weight gain and other health problems.

olive oil

sunflower oil

butter

sesame oil

fish

Fish is a low-fat source of protein and also supplies essential fatty acids, the vitamins A, D, and B12 and minerals such as iron, zinc, selenium, iodine and fluoride.

* **Lean fish** includes cod, haddock, coley, plaice, sole, monkfish and shark. White fish flesh is generally low in fat and calories, and is a useful source of protein and iron for people watching their weight or saturated fat intake. The vitamins A and D are stored in the liver of cod and so the flesh contains little but it is high in B12. If eaten regularly, the iron found in fish flesh may also help to prevent iron deficiency anaemia in women who do not eat meat.

* **Oily fish** includes salmon, trout, mackerel, fresh tuna, herring, sardines and pilchards. They are higher in fat than lean, white fish but contain omega-3 fatty acids (see box below). Oily fish contain more vitamins A and D than lean fish, both of which are required in larger amounts during pregnancy and breastfeeding.

* **Shellfish** includes oysters, scallops, crab, lobster, mussels and prawns. They are excellent low-fat sources of protein and contain useful minerals. Shellfish are generally high in selenium and also contain iodine and fluoride. Oysters are one of the richest sources of zinc. Some shellfish are relatively high in cholesterol and sodium, but at the levels they are normally eaten this does not pose a health threat.

* **Canned fish** such as sardines, pilchards and salmon often contain small soft bones that are usually eaten along with the flesh, which means that they make an important contribution to calcium intake (especially among women who don't eat dairy foods). Fish canned in oil is higher in fat and calories, so choose fish canned in brine or water. If you have high blood pressure, buy fish that are in springwater rather than brine as brine has a higher sodium content. Canned tuna is not classified as an oily fish as the processing removes most of omega-3 fats (other canned fish aren't affected in this way).

FOCUS ON OMEGA-3 FATTY ACIDS

* Omega-3 fatty acids are abundant in oily fish as well as in linseed, soya bean and rapeseed oils. A good mix of all the essential fatty acids is vital for hormone production, healthy skin and hair, as well as healthy immune and nervous systems. Omega-3 fatty acids are particularly necessary for the development of a baby's brain and eyes. Pregnant women should eat oily fish at least once a week to ensure an adequate intake.

* These fatty acids may also help reduce inflammation, the tendency for blood to clot and have also been found to aid the treatment of heart disease, psoriasis and arthritis.

sardines

sole

haddock

trout

prawns

tuna

mussels

cod

salmon

meat, poultry and eggs

These foods are good sources of high-quality protein, iron, zinc, magnesium and B vitamins. However, some varieties are relatively high in saturated fat.

* **Meat** – It is recommended that you limit your intake of red meat (beef, lamb and pork) and processed meats (eg burgers and sausages) to a maximum of 90g (3oz) per day. These foods are relatively high in saturated fat and high intakes may contribute to an increased risk of heart disease and cancer. Therefore always choose lean cuts of meat, trim off any visible fat and cook with as little added fat as possible (eg grill, stir fry or roast). Red meat is rich in zinc and pork is rich in vitamin B1 but meat products often have a high sodium (salt) content, which can be harmful.

* **Poultry** – Turkey and chicken are good sources of protein and B vitamins. Most of the fat in poultry is found just under the skin, so remove it before cooking to significantly reduce fat and calories. Duck and goose can contain more fat than chicken or turkey but also contains more iron, zinc and vitamin B12.

* **Liver and kidney** – These foods are rich sources of most vitamins and minerals, including vitamins A and B12, folate, iron, biotin, selenium and zinc, so even small amounts of liver and kidney can boost your intake of many nutrients. Liver and kidney are slightly higher in fat (and much higher in cholesterol) than other meats, but can be eaten in moderation as part of a low-fat diet. However, pregnant women and those trying to become pregnant should avoid eating liver and liver products (pâté, liverwurst) because a high intake of vitamin A may cause birth defects.

* **Eggs** provide protein, B vitamins, iron, zinc and vitamins A, D and E. They also contain some biotin and choline, which may be important for healthy skin and hair. Although eggs contain cholesterol, healthy women who don't have a high blood cholesterol level can safely eat an egg a day as part of a healthy diet. Do avoid frying eggs as this significantly increases the amount of fat and calories. Pregnant women should avoid raw or undercooked eggs and foods containing them (eg fresh mayonnaise) because of the risk of salmonella poisoning.

FOCUS ON IRON

* There are two types of iron – haem iron supplied by meat, fish and meat products and non-haem iron found in plant foods. Haem iron is much more readily absorbed than non-haem so eating moderate amounts of lean meat and fish is a good way to ensure you're getting enough.

lean lamb

hen's egg

chicken

lean beef fillet

vegetables

Because they're low in fat, high in fibre and packed with vitamins, minerals, antioxidants and other phytochemicals, vegetables are the key to optimum health.

The best way to get the most from vegetables is to eat a wide variety of different colours to get a good mix of all the nutrients and phytochemicals.

* **Green vegetables** – Broccoli, Brussels sprouts, green beans, cabbage, kohl rabi, spinach, kale, pak choi and cauliflower all belong to the cruciferous family (Brassica genus) of vegetables that contain a number of phytochemicals including indoles, isothyocynates and sulphuraphane, which may inhibit the action of cancer-causing agents. Broccoli is also a good source of folate, vitamin C and beta-carotene. Other green leafy vegetables such as spinach, watercress and kale are good sources of calcium, folate, riboflavin and potassium. Eating plenty of calcium-rich leafy vegetables may be important for women who do not eat dairy products.

* **Alliums** – This family of vegetables includes onion, garlic, leeks and chives. They all contain sulphur compounds known as allyl sulphides, which gives them their distinctive taste and smell. Not only do these vegetables add flavour and aroma to foods, they also provide many valuable compounds. For example, onions contain the flavonoid quercetin, which protects against heart disease and helps reduce blood clotting. Garlic is reputed to have antibacterial properties that protect against infection and regular intake may also reduce blood cholesterol levels.

* **Red and orange vegetables** – These vegetables include carrots, red peppers (capsicum) and pumpkin. They provide good amounts of the antioxidant beta-carotene. Some studies have shown that women taking the contraceptive pill have lower blood levels of beta-carotene and may benefit from eating extra 'orange/red' vegetables. Red peppers and chillies are also an excellent source of vitamin C and other antioxidant compounds. Tomatoes (including tinned, tomato sauce and paste) are rich in the carotenoid lycopene, which is a very powerful antioxidant.

FOCUS ON GINGER

* Ginger is a vegetable traditionally used as a spice and it has been found to contain antioxidants. It is also believed to have anti-inflammatory and pain-relieving properties that may help relieve muscle aches and rheumatoid arthritis. Ginger has been used as a traditional medicine for treating coughs and colds too. It may also help to alleviate nausea and may therefore be useful for women in the first few months of pregnancy.

ginger

celery

watercress

fine green beans

broccoli

carrots

cabbage

brussels sprouts

pumpkin

fruit

Fruit is packed with the antioxidant vitamin C plus carotenoids, folate and fibre. It is also low in fat, has a low calorie density and can be a great energy-boosting snack.

* **Citrus fruit** such as oranges, lemons and grapefruit are rich in vitamin C and also contain other antioxidant compounds like beta-cryptoxanthan. Having a glass of orange of juice or eating fresh oranges after a meal provides women with folate and vitamin C to aid iron absorption.

* **Berries** – Raw strawberries provide some beta-carotene and can contain almost as much vitamin C as fresh oranges. They are also rich in potassium and contain soluble fibre and ellagic acid, an antioxidant that has been shown to have a potent anti-cancer effect. Cranberries have antioxidant, antibacterial and anti-inflammatory effects. Studies suggest that drinking 300ml (9½fl oz) of cranberry juice daily may help women prone to cystitis. Blueberries provide some vitamin C and can be used to treat urinary tract infections.

* **Exotic fruit** includes mango, star fruit, guava, passion fruit, pomegranates, kiwi fruit and pawpaw. Mango and paw-paw are rich sources of vitamin C and carotenoids, which may reduce the risk of cervical cancer. Kiwi fruit and pineapple are also rich in vitamin C and potassium.

* **Avocados** are an excellent source of potassium, folate and vitamin E. Although they are relatively high in fat (20 percent), most of the fat is monounsaturated and so avocados can be eaten in moderation as part of a healthy diet. Research studies have shown that using a small amount of avocado in place of butter or margarine can help people lower their LDL cholesterol level.

* **Bananas and plantain** are excellent sources of energy-boosting fruit sugar and also provide potassium and vitamin B6, which makes them a nourishing snack.

* **Dried fruit**, such as dates and figs, contains a concentrated source of nutrients and fruit sugar energy (they do have more calories than an equal weight of fresh fruit). Dried apricots are a great source of beta-carotene, fibre, potassium, and iron, so are a very nutritious snack.

FOCUS ON PHYTOCHEMICALS

* Phytochemicals are compounds found in plants. Most have powerful antioxidant properties, which means that they are able to neutralize free radicals (the unstable molecules that can cause cell damage). As well as protecting against heart disease, there is growing evidence that phytochemicals can lower the risk of osteoporosis, cancer and inflammatory disorders. To ensure you get enough phytochemicals, eat a wide variety of different coloured fruit and vegetables.

banana

blueberries

mango

lemon

cranberry juice

kiwi fruit

cantaloupe (rock melon)

dried apricots

avocado

dairy products and alternatives

Dairy products are great sources of protein, calcium, phosphorous and the vitamins A, D, B2 and B12. They can be high in fat but there are many low-fat varieties available.

* **Milk** – Using reduced - or low-fat milk instead of full-fat milk is a good way to cut saturated fat from your diet. Full-fat milk contains 4 percent fat, semi-skimmed 1.7 percent fat and skimmed is virtually fat-free. All contain about the same amount of calcium, but the lower the fat content, the lower the levels of fat-soluble vitamins A and D. However, you can get enough of these vitamins from other foods.

* **Soya milk** is made from soya beans and, unlike cow's or goat's milk, does not contain lactose sugar or cholesterol. Soya milk contains isoflavones, which have antioxidant effects. Consuming soya milk and other soya foods may help alleviate hot flushes in postmenopausal women. Soya milk does not naturally contain vitamin B12 or much calcium so choose calcium-fortified soya milk if you're using it in place of dairy products.

* **Cheese** – Like the milk from which it's made, cheese is a good source of calcium but can also be high in saturated fat and salt. However, many low-fat and reduced-fat varieties of cheese are now available that can be used in cooking and as part of a low-fat diet (including ricotta and cottage cheese). Pregnant women should avoid soft, ripened cheese such as Brie due to an increased risk of the listeria infection.

* **Cream** contains between 64 percent fat (clotted) and 13 percent fat (half cream). Choosing lower fat creams will cut fat and saturated fat intake, but plain yoghurt is still a much healthier choice.

* **Yoghurt** – Full-fat yoghurt contains 3–10 percent fat, whereas yoghurt made from skimmed milk has less than 1 percent fat and contains 225 mg calcium per 150 g (5 oz) pot. Live yoghurts and those containing lactobacillus cultures may help to keep your digestive system healthy by restoring natural gut bacteria. Natural yoghurt may also be a good treatment for candida (thrush).

FOCUS ON CALCIUM

* Ensuring an adequate calcium intake is one of the most important ways women of all ages can protect their bones. Consuming milk and dairy products is the best method of getting enough calcium as its absorption is enhanced by lactose, the natural sugar found in milk and milk products. The bioavailability of calcium from non-dairy foods is much lower, but it is possible to meet your requirement for calcium even if you don't eat dairy foods. Canned fish, tofu, nuts, seeds, green leafy vegetables, white bread and dried fruit all contain useful amounts of calcium.

skimmed milk

low-fat bio-yoghurt

ricotta

cream cheese

Low in fat and high in carbohydrates. Rich in vitamin C, fibre and phytochemicals. Also a source of iron, calcium, other minerals and B vitamins.

caramelized onion and potato soup with parmesan toasts

Prep time: 15 minutes, cooking time: 40 minutes, serves 4

2 tablespoons olive oil
750g (1lb 9oz) large, sweet brown onions, thinly sliced
2 tablespoons balsamic vinegar
750g (1lb 9oz) potatoes, peeled and roughly chopped

1 litre (1¾ pints) beef or vegetable stock
1 bay leaf
Salt and cracked black pepper
1–2 sheets lavash bread or flour tortilla
Olive oil spray
50g (2oz) freshly grated Parmesan cheese

Preheat the oven to Gas 7/220°C/425°F. Heat the oil in a large saucepan, add the onions and balsamic vinegar and cook over a medium heat, stirring occasionally for 20 minutes or until the onions are soft and caramelized. Add the potatoes to the pan and cook until they start to soften. Stir in the stock, 250ml (8fl oz) of water and the bay leaf and simmer this, covered, for 15 minutes or until the potato is soft. Season to taste.

To make the parmesan toasts, cut the lavash bread into triangles and spray lightly with olive oil, place onto a non-stick baking tray and sprinkle with the grated Parmesan. Bake for 10 minutes until crisp and golden. Serve the soup with the toasts leaning up against the bowls.

PER SERVING: 315kcal/1316kJ 11g protein 11g fat 45g carbohydrate 4.5g fibre 212mg calcium 2g iron 90mcg folate 40mg vitamin C

This dish contains the perfect balance of nutrients as most of the calories (54 percent) are supplied by the carbohydrates and there is less than 35 percent from fat. Onions are a source of powerful antioxidants that may help lower blood cholesterol levels and regulate immunity.

An excellent source of fibre, folate, iron, vitamin C, beta-carotene and vitamin E. Also a good source of calcium and other minerals.

red pepper and cumin hummus with vegetable crudités

Prep time: 20 minutes, cooling time: 20 minutes, cooking time: 10 minutes, serves 4–6

2 medium red peppers (capsicum)
400g (14oz) can chickpeas, rinsed and drained
4 tablespoons lemon juice
80ml (2¾fl oz) tahini
4 tablespoons extra virgin olive oil
4 cloves garlic, crushed
½ teaspoon sweet paprika
1 teaspoon ground cumin

Salt and cracked black pepper
100g (3½oz) asparagus
100g (3½oz) green beans
100g (3½oz) broccoli, cut into florets
100g (3½oz) baby corn
2 stalks celery, cut into thick batons
2 carrots, cut into thick batons

Cook the peppers on a tray under a grill set on high until their skin blisters and blackens. Transfer them to a plastic bag and set aside to cool. Then remove the skins and cut the flesh into strips. Place the peppers, chickpeas, lemon juice, tahini, 2 tablespoons water, the olive oil, garlic, paprika and cumin into a food processor and process until smooth. Season to taste with salt and pepper.

To make the crudités, steam the asparagus, beans, broccoli and corn; rinse and drain. Arrange all the vegetables in glasses or on a platter beside the hummus.

PER SERVING: 363kcal/1516kJ   12g protein   26g fat   20g carbohydrate   8g fibre 223mg calcium   5mg iron   177mcg folate   153mg vitamin C   810mcg beta-carotene 3.5mg vitamin E

Chickpeas are low in fat, high in fibre and a useful source of iron, folate, vitamin E and phytochemicals called saponins. These are thought to boost the immune system and help protect against cancer and heart disease. Tahini is sesame seed paste and is an excellent source of calcium. Combining these two ingredients with red peppers boosts beta-carotene and vitamin C content while also making a delicious light snack.

Rich in calcium, vitamin A, folate and vitamin C.
Also contains B vitamins, fibre, iron and vitamin E.

ciabatta toast with herbed caper ricotta and chargrilled asparagus

Prep time: 10 minutes, cooking time: 10 minutes, serves 4

8 slices ciabatta or crusty Italian bread

1 tablespoon olive oil

150 g (5oz) ricotta cheese

2 cloves garlic, halved

1 tablespoon chopped fresh oregano

2 tablespoons chopped drained capers

Sea salt and cracked black pepper

2 bunches asparagus, halved

2 tablespoons balsamic vinegar

200 g (7oz) cherry tomatoes

Toast or chargrill the bread on both sides until crisp and golden. Brush one side of the bread with olive oil and then rub it generously with the garlic. Cut the ricotta into thick slices and place on top of two pieces of toast. Whisk together the oil, garlic, oregano, capers and seasoning and drizzle this mixture over the ricotta.

Heat a chargrill pan to hot, drizzle the asparagus with balsamic vinegar and cook until it is bright green and tender. Add the cherry tomatoes to the pan a couple of minutes before the end and cook them until the skins burst and they soften.

Serve the toasts topped with the asparagus and tomato and plenty of black pepper.

PER SERVING: 280 kcal/1170 kJ   12 g protein   9 g fat   39 g carbohydrate   3 g fibre 198 mg calcium   2.2 g iron   155 mcg folate   23 mg vitamin C   156 mcg beta-carotene 1.6 mg vitamin E

Ricotta cheese has a third of the fat of most hard cheeses. Combining it with ciabatta produces a carbohydrate-rich dish with useful amounts of calcium. Asparagus is bursting with useful nutrients such as fibre, folate, beta-carotene, vitamins C and E and is also thought to be a mild diuretic, which may help reduce pre-menstrual bloating.

Rich in protein and also contains the B vitamins and vitamin E, as well as some fibre, iron and zinc.

chicken satays with peanut sauce

Prep time: 20 minutes, cooking time: 20 minutes, serves 4, makes 12 sticks

500g (1lb 1½ oz) chicken breast fillets, cut into thin strips

1 tablespoon soya bean oil

4 shallots, finely chopped

1 clove garlic, crushed

1 tablespoon finely chopped lemongrass

115g (4oz) light crunchy peanut butter

1 tablespoon fish sauce

1 tablespoon sweet chilli sauce

300ml (9½ fl oz) light coconut milk

4 wholemeal pitta breads, to serve

Soak 12 bamboo skewers in cold water for 30 minutes to stop them burning when they cook. Thread the chicken onto the skewers and cook them under the grill for 5–10 minutes or until tender, turning the skewers several times during cooking.

Heat the oil in a small saucepan, add the shallots, garlic and lemongrass and cook over a medium heat for 5 minutes or until the onions are soft. Add the peanut butter, fish sauce, sweet chilli sauce and coconut milk. Cook until smooth, stirring constantly, then simmer for 10 minutes or until the sauce thickens. Serve the chicken with peanut sauce and one wholemeal pitta bread per serving

PER SERVING: 558kcal/2331kJ 45g protein 21g fat 52g carbohydrate 5.9g fibre 82mg calcium 3.7mg iron

Lean, skinless chicken fillet is an excellent low-fat source of protein. Although nuts are relatively high in fat – about 50 percent fat – they provide vitamin E, protein and B vitamins and so can be a healthy part of a balanced diet if used in small amounts. Serving the satay with wholemeal pitta bread increases fibre, iron and zinc content to produce a healthy balance of nutrients.

High in vitamin C and also contains B vitamins.

orange and pink grapefruit juice with lemon ginger and honey ice cubes
Prep time: 10 minutes, serves 2

80 ml (2¾ fl oz) lemon juice
80 ml (2¾ fl oz) water
1 tablespoon finely shredded ginger
1 tablespoon honey
12 small mint leaves
300 ml (9½ fl oz) fresh orange juice
300 ml (9½ fl oz) pink grapefruit juice

Put the lemon juice, water, ginger and honey into a jug and whisk to combine. Pour into an ice cube tray and place a mint leaf on top of each cube. Freeze. Divide the ice cubes between two glasses and pour the juices in.
PER SERVING: 140 kcal/585 kJ 1.8 g protein 35 g carb 128 mg vitamin C 54 mcg folate

Rich in vitamin C, fibre and phytochemicals.

mixed berry and pineapple frappé
Prep time: 10 minutes, serves 2

200 g (7oz) fresh or frozen mixed berries (raspberries, blackberries, mulberries)
225 g (8oz) chopped pineapple
250 ml (8fl oz) pineapple juice
½ teaspoon rosewater

Place the berries, pineapple, pineapple juice and rosewater into a food liquidizer or blender and purée until smooth. Pour into two chilled glasses. Rinse the liquidizer and dry thoroughly.
PER SERVING: 122 kcal/510 kJ 2 g protein 0.5 g fat 30 g carbohydrate 4 g fibre 63 mg calcium 50 mg vitamin C

Rich in folate, beta-carotene, vitamin C and fibre

cantaloupe, beetroot, ginger and mint juice
Prep time: 5 minutes, serves 2

225 g (8oz) chopped cantaloupe (rockmelon)
500 g (1lb 2oz) beetroot, cut into wedges
2 tablespoons roughly chopped fresh ginger
2 tablespoons mint leaves

Place the ingredients one at a time into a food liquidizer or juicer and purée. Serve in chilled glasses. *Note:* There is no need to cook or peel the beetroot.
PER SERVING: 127 kcal/533 kJ 6 g protein 0.5 g fat 27 g carb 5.4 g fibre 78 mg calcium 3.7 mg iron 410 mcg folate 42 mg vitamin C 386 mcg beta-carotene

Rich in fibre, beta-carotene and vitamins C and E.

mango banana smoothies
Prep time: 5 minutes, serves 2

2 mangoes
1 banana, sliced
250 ml (8fl oz) low-fat vanilla soya milk or organic milk
2 tablespoons wheatgerm
½ teaspoon nutmeg

Roughly chop the mango flesh and place it into a food liquidizer or blender with the banana, soya milk, wheatgerm and nutmeg and blend until thick and smooth. *Note:* Add extra soya milk for a thinner smoothie.
PER SERVING: 200 kcal/840 kJ 7 g protein 3 g fat 40 g carbohydrate 5.2 g fibre

An excellent source of fibre, calcium, iron and the antioxidant vitamins A,C, E. Also contains B vitamins, zinc and other minerals.

fettucine with tomato, mozzarella and watercress pesto

Prep time: 15 minutes, cooking time: 15 minutes, serves 4

115g (4oz) firmly packed watercress leaves
115g (4oz) firmly packed basil leaves
2 cloves garlic
2 tablespoons pumpkin seeds
2 tablespoons blanched almonds
50g (2oz) grated Parmesan cheese

Sea salt and cracked black pepper
30ml (1fl oz) extra virgin olive oil
200g (7oz) cherry tomatoes, halved
200g (7oz) mozzarella balls (baby bocconcini), roughly chopped
400g (14oz) fettucine (preferably wholemeal)

Put the watercress, basil, garlic, pumpkin seeds, almonds, Parmesan and a generous pinch of salt into a food processor and process to form a smooth paste. With the motor still running, gradually add the olive oil and process until combined.

Cut the tomatoes in half and place them onto a baking tray and grill for 5–10 minutes or until they are soft and slightly dried. Roughly chop the mozzarella and stir the tomatoes through. Season with sea salt and pepper.

Cook the pasta in a large pan of rapidly boiling water until *al dente* then drain, leaving a little water in the pan to stop the pasta sticking. Add the tomato mixture and pesto to the fettucine and toss to combine.

PER SERVING: 668Kcal/2791KJ 36g protein 30g fat 67g carbohydrate 10g fibre 619mg calcium 7.4mg iron 5.4mg zinc 3.1mg vitamin E (analysis based on using wholemeal fettucine)

This carbohydrate-rich dish is packed with powerful antioxidants and one serving almost provides the total recommended daily intakes for vitamin C (mainly due to the watercress and tomatoes), calcium and vitamin E.

Pumpkin seeds and almonds are good sources of fibre, vitamins E, essential fatty acids and selenium. Using wholemeal fettucine is an excellent way to boost your fibre, B vitamin and mineral intake, while the cheeses provide calcium. Serve this dish with a salad for extra antioxidants or with a wholemeal bread roll to create a really filling meal.

An excellent source of fibre, iron, zinc, vitamin A, vitamin B12 and other B vitamins. Also contains calcium, selenium, and vitamins D and E.

grilled indian lamb cutlets with spicy carrot and chickpeas

Prep time: 20 minutes, marinating time: 30 minutes, cooking time: 15 minutes, serves 4

12 lamb cutlets
2 tablespoons Madras curry paste
115g (4oz) low-fat natural yoghurt
1 tablespoon sunflower oil
1 onion, thinly sliced
1 tablespoon grated fresh ginger
1 red chilli, finely chopped
1 teaspoon garam marsala

1 teaspoon brown mustard seeds
115g (4oz) grated carrot
400g (14oz) can chickpeas, rinsed and drained
2 tomatoes, chopped
2 tablespoon chopped fresh coriander
Salt and cracked black pepper
Mango chutney, to serve
2 x 160g (5¼oz) naan bread, to serve

Trim the lamb cutlets of any excess fat or sinew then place them into a shallow non-metallic dish. Combine the curry paste and yoghurt and pour this over the cutlets. Turn the cutlets to coat them in the marinade, cover and refrigerate for 30 minutes.

Heat the oil in a large frying pan, add the onion, ginger, chilli, garam marsala and mustard seeds and cook over a medium heat until the onion is soft and the mustard seeds begin to pop. Add the carrot, chickpeas, tomatoes and 3 tablespoons of water, bring to the boil, then reduce the heat and simmer until most of the liquid has been absorbed. Stir through the coriander and season with salt and pepper. Cook the cutlets on a barbecue or under the grill, turning them once, until tender. Serve the cutlets with the carrot and chickpeas, a generous dollop of mango chutney and oven-warmed naan bread.

PER SERVING: 748kcal/3126kJ 58g protein 33g fat 59g carbohydrate 5.6g fibre
277mg calcium 6.6mg iron 7mg zinc 28mcg selenium 4.6mcg vitamin B12 400mcg vitamin A 1mcg vitamin D 4mg vitamin E

Lamb is traditionally considered a fatty meat, but lean cuts are now available and a fillet of lamb can contain as little as 8 percent fat. Combining pulses with meat is a good way to reduce the fat and increase the fibre and antioxidant content of a dish. By using lots of fresh herbs and spices you can add flavour to a dish without having to use extra fat or salt.

An excellent source of iron, fibre, B vitamins and the vitamins C and E. Also contains some zinc, calcium, selenium and vitamin A.

stir fried sesame beef with mixed greens and almonds

Prep time: 15 minutes, cooking time: 15 minutes, serves 4

1 tablespoon peanut oil

1 teaspoon sesame oil

½ teaspoon five spice powder

500g (1lb 2oz) rump steak, thinly sliced

1 tablespoon grated fresh ginger

1 clove garlic, crushed

6 spring onions, sliced

50g (2oz) blanched almonds

1 bunch broccolini, roughly chopped

1 bunch Chinese broccoli, roughly chopped

200g (7oz) mangetout (snow peas)

2 tablespoons oyster sauce

1 tablespoon low-salt soy sauce

1 teaspoon honey

300g (11oz) brown rice (raw weight), to serve

Heat the oils and five spice powder in a wok over a high heat, cook the meat in two batches until browned then remove. Add the ginger, garlic, spring onions, almonds and 2 tablespoons of water to the wok and stir fry for 2 minutes. Return the meat to the wok along with the greens, oyster sauce, soy sauce and honey and toss until the greens have wilted. Serve hot with rice.

Note: If broccolini is not available you can use 250g (9oz) of broccoli florets instead.

PER SERVING: 595kcal/2487kJ 41g protein 19g fat 70g carbohydrate 6g fibre 159mg calcium 6.5mg iron 7.4mg zinc 1.1mg vitamin B6 2.9mcg vitamin B12 175mcg folate 89mg vitamin C 5mg vitamin E

This is a nutrient-packed dish supplying a high proportion of women's daily requirements for many nutrients. For example, one serving provides more than the recommended daily intake of vitamins E, C, B12, B6, B1 and niacin. Stir frying is a convenient low-fat cooking method and this dish contains well below the maximum recommendation of 35 percent of calories from fat, which means it's also healthy for your heart.

Low in fat, carbohydrate-rich and a good source of fibre, iron and antioxidant vitamins A, C and E. Also contains B vitamins and calcium.

fusilli with spicy italian sauce

Prep time: 10 minutes, cooking time: 20 minutes, serves 4

2 tablespoons extra virgin olive oil
2 cloves garlic, crushed
1 onion, chopped
2 red chillies, finely chopped
100g (3½oz) Parma ham, chopped
1 small aubergine (eggplant), cut into cubes
1 red pepper (capsicum), chopped

2 tablespoons baby capers, chopped
100g (3½oz) Kalamata olives
800g (1¾lb) chopped tomatoes
1 teaspoon sugar
Salt and cracked black pepper
500g (1lb 2oz) fusilli

Heat the oil in a large fry pan, add the garlic, onion and chilli and cook over a medium heat for 5 minutes or until the onion is soft. Add the ham and aubergine and cook until the aubergine is golden brown. Add the pepper, caper and olives and cook until the pepper softens. Stir in the tomatoes and sugar and bring to the boil, reduce the heat and simmer for 10 minutes or until the sauce thickens slightly. Season with salt and cracked black pepper. Cook the fusilli in a large pan of rapidly boiling water until *al dente*, then drain well. Add the fusilli to the sauce and toss to combine.

PER SERVING: 633kcal/2645kJ 26g protein 14g fat 107g carbohydrate 8g fibre 90mg calcium 4mg iron 92mcg folate 96mg vitamin C 370mcg vitamin A 3.7mg vitamin E

Pasta is not fattening, it's the sauces put with it that often add fat and calories. With most of the calories coming from starchy carbohydrates, and only 20 percent from fat, this dish is low in fat and contains a healthy balance of nutrients. Olives are rich in monounsaturates, which, if used in small quantities to replace saturated fat in the diet, can help lower blood cholesterol levels. Peppers, tomatoes and chilli combine to provide a protective dose of antioxidants beta-carotene and vitamin C, while the olives and tomatoes also supply useful amounts of vitamin E.

An excellent source of protein, B vitamins, iron, zinc and vitamin E. Also provides fibre, calcium, vitamin C and potassium.

poached chicken and greens with sesame miso dressing

Prep time: 15 minutes, cooking time: 30 minutes, serves 4

4 chicken breast fillets
3 black peppercorns
3 slices fresh ginger
3 spring onions, sliced
200g (7oz) mangetout (snow peas)
200g (7oz) asparagus, cut into 4cm (½in) lengths
100g (3½oz) green beans, cut into 4cm (1½in) lengths

For the sesame miso dressing
1 teaspoon sesame oil
2 teaspoons white miso
3 tablespoons mirin/sherry
3 tablespoons low-salt soy sauce
2 tablespoons seasoned rice vinegar
2 tablespoons black sesame seeds
700g (24oz) pilau rice (cooked weight), to serve

Trim the chicken breast fillets of any excess fat and sinew. Half fill a large deep frying pan with water, add the peppercorns, ginger and spring onions and the chicken. Simmer them gently for 20 minutes or until the chicken is tender. Remove the chicken and allow it to cool slightly.

Steam the mangetout, asparagus and beans until tender then arrange them on a platter. Shred the chicken in thin strips and arrange these on top of the vegetables. Put the dressing ingredients into a small pan and whisk this over a medium heat until the miso dissolves. Drizzle the dressing over the salad and sprinkle on the black sesame seeds. To get the right balance of nutrients, it is best to serve this dish with pilau rice.

PER SERVING: 617kcal/2579kJ 42g protein 26g fat 51g carbohydrate 4.2g fibre 140mg calcium 127mg magnesium 3.8mg iron 3g zinc 26mg niacin 1mg vitamin B6 150mcg folate 38mg vitamin C 6.5mg vitamin E

Chicken is a great low-fat source of protein, B vitamins, magnesium, iron and zinc and poaching is a good way to cook it without adding extra fat to the meat. Sesame seeds are an excellent source of calcium.

An excellent source of omega-3 essential fatty acids, vitamins E, A, C and D, plus folate and the other B vitamins as well as fibre.

tuna steaks with smashed sweet potato and lime seed butter

Prep time: 20 minutes, chilling time: 30 minutes, cooking time: 30 minutes, serves 4

50 g (2oz) omega essential fatty acid spread or soya-based spread
2 teaspoons grated lime zest
2 tablespoons lime juice
½ teaspoon honey
1 tablespoon snipped fresh chives
1 tablespoon roughly chopped sunflower seeds

750g (1lb 8oz) orange sweet potato
125ml (4fl oz) orange juice
Pinch saffron threads
Salt and black cracked pepper
1 tablespoon sunflower oil
4 tuna steaks (approx 125g/4½ oz)
2 bunches asparagus

Combine the soya butter, lime zest, lime juice, honey, chives and sunflower seeds in a bowl. Shape the mixture into a log and wrap in cling film (plastic wrap) and chill for 30 minutes or until firm.

Cook the sweet potato in a large pan of boiling water until soft, drain and stir in the orange juice and saffron and season with salt and pepper. Mash until smooth, cover and keep warm.

Heat the oil in a large frying pan, add the tuna steaks and cook over a medium-high heat until cooked to your liking (cooking time will vary depending upon the thickness of the tuna steaks). Then steam the asparagus until bright green and tender.

Serve the tuna on top of the sweet potatoes with a slice of the lime seed butter, accompanied by the steamed asparagus.

PER SERVING: 460kcal/1927kJ 36g protein 22g fat 57g carbohydrate 6g fibre 100mg calcium 3.9mg iron 77mcg selenium 210mcg folate 119mg vitamin C 1312mcg vitamin A 12.5mg vitamin E 9mcg vitamin D

Fresh tuna is an oily fish and, therefore, contains omega-3 essential fatty acids (canned tuna loses many of these oils during processing and is not considered 'oily'). These fats may help prevent heart disease and are essential for pregnant women. Tuna is an excellent source of selenium, which is a powerful antioxidant that works with vitamin E to protect the body from free radicals.

An excellent low-fat source of iron, selenium and fibre. Also contains calcium, folate, other B vitamins and vitamin A.

chicken burgers filled with ricotta and spinach

Prep time: 15 minutes, chilling time: 30 minutes, cooking time: 30 minutes, serves 4

4-day-old thick slices wholemeal bread
100g (3½oz) baby spinach leaves
100g (3½oz) low-fat ricotta
Salt and cracked black pepper
Pinch nutmeg
500g (1lb 2oz) chicken mince
1 red onion, grated

2 tablespoons chopped fresh coriander
1 teaspoon ground cumin
1 teaspoon ground allspice
Olive oil spray
Wholemeal bread rolls, to serve
Mixed lettuce leaves, to serve
Homemade chutney, to serve

Remove the crusts from the bread and break it into bite size pieces. Cover the pieces with warm water and allow to stand for 10 minutes or until the bread has absorbed the water. Squeeze out any excess moisture.

Wash the spinach leaves, put them into a saucepan, cover and cook over a medium heat until the leaves wilt. Allow to cool and squeeze out any excess moisture. Roughly chop the spinach, then combine with the ricotta, salt, pepper and nutmeg.

Put the chicken mince, bread, onion, coriander and spices into a bowl and mix to combine. Divide the mixture into four and shape each portion into round flat patties (this is best done with wetted hands). Make a hole in the centre of each patty, taking care not to go all the way through to the other side, and fill the hole with some of the ricotta and spinach mixture. Shape a little of the chicken mixture over the hole to enclose the filling. Cover and refrigerate for 30 minutes.

Cook the patties in a lightly oiled non-stick frying pan over a medium heat for 15–20 minutes or until cooked through. Serve the patties on toasted wholemeal rolls, dressed with lettuce and finished with your favourite homemade chutney or relish.

Note: These burgers are delicious hot or cold and can be made into small meatballs, which are perfect to serve at cocktail parties.

PER SERVING: 422 kcal/1767 kJ 39g protein 8g fat 56g carbohydrate 6g fibre 185mg calcium 5mg iron 43.6mcg selenium 115mcg folate 248mcg vitamin A

With less than 3 percent fat and most of the calories from fibre-rich carbohydrates, this dish contains a great balance of nutrients. Chicken mince is a low-fat versatile ingredient and can be used in place of beef mince in many dishes.

An excellent source of vitamin C and beta-carotene.
Also contains fibre, iron and folate.

mixed vegetable and black bean noodle stir fry

Prep time: 15 minutes, cooking time: 15 minutes, serves 4–6

200g (7oz) dried rice stick noodles
1 tablespoon peanut oil
2 teaspoons sesame oil
1 onion, cut into thin wedges
1 clove garlic, crushed
1 tablespoon grated fresh ginger
1 carrot, thinly sliced

1 red pepper (capsicum), thinly sliced
100g (3½oz) baby corn
300g (11oz) Chinese broccoli, roughly chopped
2 tablespoons black bean sauce
1 teaspoon sugar
2 tablespoons Chinese rice wine vinegar

Put the rice noodles into a large bowl and cover with boiling water. Allow to stand for 10 minutes or until the noodles are soft, drain well and pat dry. Heat the oil in a wok, add the onion, garlic and ginger and stir fry for 3 minutes or until the onion softens. Add the carrot, pepper, and corn and stir fry until the vegetables are bright in colour. Add the Chinese broccoli and noodles and toss until the broccoli wilts.

Put the black bean sauce, sugar and rice wine vinegar into a jug and whisk to combine. Add to the wok and stir fry until the sauce coats the noodles and is heated through.

**PER SERVING: 303kcal/1266kJ 8g protein 6g fat 53g carbohydrate 4g fibre
81mg calcium 3mg iron 123mcg folate 134mg vitamin C 615mcg beta-carotene**

This dish is absolutely bursting with vitamin C. As well as being an antioxidant, vitamin C increases the absorption of iron from non-meat sources, which makes this dish an excellent choice for vegetarians. One serving also provides the entire recommended daily intake of beta-carotene (pro-vitamin A), which is especially important for pregnant and breastfeeding women. The broccoli and baby corn also supply useful amounts of folate.

Low in fat, high in carbohydrates and an excellent source of fibre, vitamins C, E, beta-carotene, folate, iron, potassium and calcium.

tofu and black eye bean mexican casserole

Prep time: 20 minutes, soaking time: overnight, cooking time: 1 hour, serves 4–6

175g (6oz) black eye beans
1½ tablespoons olive oil
2 onions, chopped
1 red chilli, finely chopped
2 carrots, chopped
1 red pepper (capsicum), cut into cubes
500g (1lb 2oz) organic firm tofu,
cut into cubes

3 tablespoons tomato purée double
concentrate (tomato paste)
1 tablespoon cider vinegar
25g (1oz) brown sugar
1 teaspoon French mustard
400g (14oz) can chopped tomatoes
1 bay leaf
4 x 55g (2oz) flour tortillas, to serve

Cook the beans in hot water for 40 minutes or until just tender, then drain them well. Heat the oil in a large pan, add the onion, chilli and cook over a medium heat for 5 minutes or until soft. Add the carrot and pepper and cook for a further 5 minutes or until they soften. Next add the tofu, tomato purée, vinegar, sugar, mustard, tomatoes, bay leaf and beans and simmer uncovered for 15 minutes or until the sauce has thickened. Serve hot with flour tortillas.

Note: This recipe is delicious served with low-fat sour cream and homemade guacamole.

PER SERVING: 516kcal/2157kJ 28g protein 11g fat 81g carbohydrate 9g fibre 788mg calcium 7mg iron 340mcg folate 87mg vitamin C 888mcg beta-carotene 4mg vitamin E

One serving of this vegetarian dish contains more than the daily requirement for many nutrients including calcium, vitamin C, beta-carotene and vitamin E. It's high in fibre and is an excellent low-fat source of energy. Tofu (soya bean curd) is a nutritious, iron- and calcium-rich alternative to meat and its phytoestrogen content may help reduce risk of cancers if consumed regularly.

Rich in fibre, vitamins C, E and beta-carotene, plus protective phytochemicals. Also a source of calcium, iron, other minerals, folate and other B vitamins.

crunchy cabbage, carrot and almond slaw

Prep time: 20 minutes, cooking time: nil, serves 4

115g (4oz) finely shredded red cabbage
115g (4oz) finely shredded Chinese cabbage
2 carrots, cut into thin matchsticks
2 stalks celery, thinly sliced
1 red pepper (capsicum), cut into thin strips
3 spring onions, thinly sliced
75g (3oz) flaked almonds, toasted
100g (3½oz) boiled noodles

For the dressing
1 small red chilli, finely chopped
3 tablespoons lime juice
1 tablespoon fish sauce
1 tablespoon sesame oil
1 tablespoon brown sugar

Put the cabbages, carrots, celery, red pepper, spring onions and almonds into a large salad bowl and toss to combine. Whisk together the chilli, lime juice, fish sauce, sesame oil and brown sugar until the sugar dissolves. Pour the dressing over the salad and toss to combine. Allow this to stand for 15 minutes before serving. Finally, add the noodles and quickly toss before serving immediately.

PER SERVING: 212kcal/885kJ 6g protein 13g fat 18g carbohydrate 5g fibre 110mg calcium 1.4mg iron 60mcg folate 96mg vitamin C 833mcg beta-carotene 5mg vitamin E

Using raw vegetables in a dish is a great way to preserve nutrients that may otherwise be lost during cooking. One serving of this fibre-rich dish contains more than the recommended daily intake of vitamin A in the form of beta-carotene. Serve this salad with some wholemeal pitta bread to provide a more substantial meal.

An excellent source of fibre, vitamins C, E and beta-carotene. Also contains iron, calcium, folate and other B vitamins.

vegetable stew with cheesy herb dumplings

Prep time: 20 minutes, cooking time: 40 minutes, serves 4

2 tablespoons olive oil
1 leek, thinly sliced
1 red pepper (capsicum), chopped
2 cloves garlic, crushed
1 red chilli, finely chopped
1 teaspoon ground cumin
1 teaspoon ground coriander
Pinch saffron threads
2 carrots, cut into large chunks
500g (1lb 2oz) potato, cut into chunks
500g (1lb 2oz) orange sweet potato, cut into chunks

2 courgettes (zucchini), cut into thick slices
2 x 400g (14oz) can peeled tomatoes
1 bay leaf
115g (4oz) marinated black olives
For the dumplings
115g (4oz) self raising flour
25g (1oz) butter, chopped
2 tablespoons finely grated Parmesan
2 tablespoons finely shredded basil
60ml (2fl oz) low-fat milk
Sea salt and cracked black pepper

Heat the oil in a large saucepan, add the leek and red pepper and cook over a medium heat for 5 minutes or until soft and golden brown. Add the garlic, chilli and spices and cook until the spices are fragrant. Add the carrot, potato, sweet potato and courgettes and stir to coat them with the spices. Cover and cook until the vegetable start to soften. Next, add the tomatoes, bay leaf, olives and 250ml (8fl oz) of water, bring to the boil, reduce the heat and simmer for 25 minutes or until the vegetables are fully soft.

Meanwhile, make the dumplings. Put the flour and butter into a bowl and rub in the butter using your fingertips until the mixture resembles fine breadcrumbs. Stir in the Parmesan, basil and milk using a flat-bladed knife until the mixture clumps together. Season with sea salt and pepper. Gather the mixture into a ball using you hands, then drop tablespoons of the dumpling mixture into the stew. Work quickly to ensure the dumplings will cook evenly. Cover and cook for 10–15 minutes or until a skewer comes out clean when inserted into the centre of each dumpling.

PER SERVING: 517kcal/2162kJ   13g protein   18g fat   82g carbohydrate   10g fibre   295mg calcium   4mg iron   149mcg folate   143mg vitamin C   1890mcg vitamin A   9mg vitamin E

This colourful vegetarian dish provides plenty of fibre and a range of healthy plant compounds, including antioxidants and other cancer-protective elements.

Rich in fibre, vitamins C, E and beta-carotene, iron and calcium. Also a good source of zinc and folate.

pumpkin, broccoli and chickpea salad with sweet yoghurt dressing

Prep time: 15 minutes, cooking time: 40 minutes, serves 4–6

750g (1lb 9oz) Jap pumpkin or butternut squash, cut into large pieces
400g (14oz) can chickpeas, rinsed and drained
1 tablespoon soya bean oil
3 tablespoons sweet chilli sauce

300g (11oz) broccoli, cut into florets and steamed
50g (2oz) pepitas/shelled pumpkin seeds
2 tablespoons chopped fresh coriander
2 tablespoons low-fat plain yoghurt

Preheat the oven to Gas 6/200°C/400°F. Put the pumpkin and chickpeas into a roasting tin, pour over the combined oil and 2 tablespoons of the sweet chilli sauce and toss to coat. Roast for 40 minutes or until the pumpkin is soft. Transfer to a salad bowl and fold through the cooked broccoli, pepitas and coriander.

Whisk together the yoghurt and remaining sweet chilli sauce. Drizzle this mixture over the salad and gently toss to combine.

PER SERVING: 240kcal/1004kJ 13g protein 12g fat 22g carbohydrate 7g fibre
170mg calcium 90mg magnesium 5mg iron 2mg zinc 98mcg folate 94mg vitamin C
240mcg vitamin A 5mg vitamin E

This vegetable dish makes an excellent accompaniment to poultry and fish or as a light meal if served with crusty bread. Pumpkin (squash) is a good source of antioxidants beta-carotene and vitamin E. Its seeds (called pepitas when shelled) are a useful source of iron, magnesium and zinc. Although they are relatively high in fat, it's mostly unsaturated, and they are usually only used in small amounts. One serving of this dish also provides nearly a half of the recommended daily intake of fibre (from the chickpeas, broccoli and pumpkin).

A rich source of fibre, calcium, essential fatty acids, vitamins A, C and E. Also contains iron, folate and other B vitamins.

spinach, apricot and avocado salad with mixed seed dressing

Prep time: 15 minutes, cooking time: nil, serves 6

150g (5oz) baby spinach leaves
175g (6oz) trimmed watercress
100g (3½oz) dried apricots, roughly chopped
100g (3½oz) Parmesan, shaved
2 avocados, cut into thick slices
100g (3½oz) mung bean sprouts
3 tablespoons sunflower seeds

2 tablespoons sesame seeds
1 tablespoon extra virgin olive oil
2 tablespoons orange juice
2 tablespoons balsamic vinegar
1 teaspoon honey
2 cloves garlic, crushed
240g (8½oz) French stick, to serve

Arrange the spinach, watercress, apricots, Parmesan and avocado onto a large salad platter. Combine the sprouts and seeds and sprinkle them over the salad. Whisk together the oil, orange juice, balsamic vinegar, honey and garlic and drizzle over the salad, gently tossing to combine. Serve immediately with 40g (1½oz) of French stick per person.

PER SERVING: 420kcal/1755kJ 17g protein 25g fat 35g carbohydrate 6g fibre 405mg calcium 4mg iron 19mcg selenium 72mcg folate 31mg vitamin C 354mcg vitamin A 6mg vitamin E

Using seeds in salads is an excellent way of boosting your intake of vitamins, minerals, essential fatty acids and phytochemicals. Sunflower seeds are a good source of vitamin E and selenium, whereas sesame seeds are rich in calcium – although it is less well absorbed from them than it is from dairy products.

An excellent low-fat source of protein, iron, zinc and B vitamins. Also contains fibre, calcium, magnesium, and vitamins A and E.

pork, apple and bay kebabs with dried fruit couscous

Prep time: 20 minutes, cooking time: 15 minutes, serves 4

500g (1lb 2oz) pork fillet, cut into 3cm (1¼in) cubes

1–2 firm red apples, cut into small wedges (skin left on)

16 fresh bay leaves

115g (4oz) couscous

1 cinnamon stick

1 teaspoon ground cumin

1 teaspoon ground coriander

150g (5oz) mixed dried fruit, chopped

500ml (16fl oz) boiling vegetable stock

30g (1¼oz) butter

2 tablespoons chopped fresh coriander

3 whole lemons, cut into 4 wedges, to serve

Soak 12 bamboo skewers in cold water for 30 minutes to stop them from catching alight when they cook. Next, thread the pork, apples and bay leaves onto the skewers.

Put the couscous, cinnamon, spices and dried fruit into a bowl, pour over the stock and allow to stand for 10 minutes or until the liquid is absorbed. Then fork through the butter and coriander. Cover the couscous and keep it warm.

Place the skewers on a barbecue or under a hot grill, turning them a couple of times during cooking until the pork is tender. Serve the kebabs beside the couscous with wedges of lemon.

PER SERVING: 562kcal/2351kJ 34g protein 15g fat 76g carbohydrate 2g fibre 63mg calcium 7mg iron 2mg zinc 2mg vitamin B1

Pork fillet can contain as little as 4 percent fat and is an excellent source of B vitamins, zinc and iron. This recipe contains a healthy balance of nutrients as more than half the calories are from carbohydrates and less than 30 percent from fat. Serving the dish with plenty of green vegetables will further boost the fibre, folate, vitamin C and calcium levels.

An excellent source of fibre, iron, zinc, vitamin C, folate and B vitamins. Also contains selenium, calcium and vitamin E.

beef fillet with balsamic onions and parsnip and pea puree

Prep time: 15 minutes, cooking time: 40 minutes, serves 4

750g (1lb 10oz) parsnips
115g (4oz) frozen mint peas
20g (1oz) light sour cream
Salt and cracked black pepper
4 x 150g (5oz) lean sirloin steaks
1½ tablespoons olive oil

6 bulb spring onions, halved
2 tablespoons balsamic vinegar
1 tablespoon honey cup mustard
250ml (8fl oz) beef stock
800g (1¾lb) new potatoes, to serve

Peel and chop the parsnips and put them into a large pan, cover with water and cook for 15 minutes or until nearly soft. Add the peas and cook for a further 5 minutes or until soft. Take off the heat and add the sour cream before seasoning with salt and pepper. Use an upright blender to blend the mixture into a smooth purée.

Trim any fat or sinew from the steaks. Heat one tablespoon of oil in a large frying pan, add the onions and cook for 5 minutes, then add the vinegar, stock and mustard and simmer for 15 minutes or until the onions are soft and the liquid has reduced by half. Heat the remaining oil in a large frying pan; add the steak and cook, turning once until cooked to your liking. Serve the steaks topped with the onions on a bed of the parsnip and pea purée and accompanied by new potatoes.

PER SERVING: 530kcal/2214kJ 42g protein 15g fat 60g carbohydrate 12g fibre
134mg calcium 5mg iron 7mg zinc 17mcg selenium 2mg vitamin B6 3mg vitamin B12
261mcg folate 72mg vitamin C 2mg vitamin E

Lean beef fillet can contain as little as 5 percent fat and is rich in protein, iron, zinc, selenium and vitamin B12. Remember that iron from meat (haem iron) is more easily absorbed than that from vegetables so women with heavy periods or low iron stores may benefit from including moderate amounts of lean red meat in their diet.

Low in fat, carbohydrate-rich and a good source of fibre, iron, selenium, calcium, and vitamins C, E, folate, as well as other B vitamins.

smoked salmon and asparagus risotto

Prep time: 15 minutes, cooking time: 35 minutes, serves 4

1 litre (1¾ pints) vegetable stock
125 ml (4fl oz) white wine
2 tablespoons olive oil
2 leeks, thinly sliced
2 sprigs lemon thyme
350g (12oz) Arborio rice

200g (7oz) strips of smoked salmon
300g (11oz) asparagus, cut into 3cm (1¼in) lengths
1 tablespoon snipped fresh chives
Zest and juice of 1 lemon
Salt and cracked black pepper

Heat the stock and wine in a saucepan, bring to the boil, reduce and keep at a low simmer. Heat the oil in a large saucepan, add the leeks and cook over a medium heat for 5 minutes or until soft. Add the lemon thyme and Arborio rice, cook for 1 minute or until the rice is translucent, stirring constantly.

Add 125 ml (4fl oz) of the hot liquid to the rice, stirring constantly until the liquid is absorbed. Add half the smoked salmon. Continue adding the stock 125 ml (4fl oz) at a time until you have only 125 ml of the liquid left. Add the remaining smoked salmon, asparagus, chives and remaining liquid then cook until the asparagus is bright green and tender. Add the lemon zest and juice and season with salt and pepper.

Note: Any leftover risotto can be shaped into patties and refrigerated overnight. Just cook the patties in a lightly oiled pan until crisp and golden and heated through.

PER SERVING: 495 kcal/2069 kJ 22g protein 9g fat 81g carbohydrate 3g fibre 56mg calcium 2mg iron 22mcg selenium 192mcg folate 24mg vitamin C 134mcg vitamin A 2mg vitamin E

Rice is an excellent low-fat source of energy. Cooking and serving it with wine, fresh herbs and lemon juice adds flavour without using salt. Smoked salmon is a good source of omega-3 fatty acids while asparagus is rich in folate and a useful source of vitamins C, E and beta-carotene. Serve this dish with plenty of salad or vegetables for extra vitamins and phytochemicals.

Rich in vitamins C, E and beta-carotene, fibre, folate and phytochemicals. Also a source of iron, calcium and other minerals.

beans and cabbage in tomato cinnamon sauce with pine nuts

Prep: 10 minutes, cooking time: 40 minutes, serves 4

500g (1lb 2oz) green beans

1 tablespoon olive oil

1 large onion, sliced

3 cloves garlic, crushed

1 teaspoon ground cinnamon

225g (8oz) shredded green cabbage

4 ripe tomatoes (500g/1lb 2oz), chopped

Salt and cracked black pepper

2 tablespoons toasted pine nuts, to serve

Top and tail the beans and cut them in half. Heat the oil in a large frying pan, add the onion and garlic and cook over a medium heat for 5 minutes or until the onion is soft. Add the cinnamon and cook until fragrant. Then add the beans and cabbage and cook for 2 minutes, stir in 250ml (8fl oz) of water and the tomatoes. Season with salt and cracked black pepper and simmer for 30 minutes or until the sauce is reduced by half. Serve sprinkled with the toasted pine nuts.

PER SERVING: 166kcal/694kJ 6g protein 9g fat 16g carbohydrate 6g fibre 108mg calcium 3mg iron 173mcg folate 67mg vitamin C 239mcg beta-carotene 3mg vitamin E

Green beans make an excellent accompaniment to a meal – they're rich in folate, iron and calcium. Tomatoes provide vitamin C, E and beta-carotene along with lycopene – a carotenoid thought to help reduce the risk of cancers and heart disease. Pine nuts are a useful source of vitamin E, zinc and magnesium although they are high in (mostly unsaturated) fat. If you're watching your weight, the nuts can easily be cut from the recipe.

Low in fat, high in carbohydrate and an excellent source of fibre, calcium, vitamins A, C and E, potassium and folate.

warm roast vegetables with chilli mozzarella

Prep time: 15 minutes, cooking time: 50 minutes, serves 4–6

500g (1lb 2oz) new potatoes
3 parsnips, peeled and quartered
500g (1lb 2oz) orange sweet potato
350g (12 oz) baby carrots
6 pickling onions
Olive oil spray
12 unpeeled garlic cloves

1 teaspoon harissa
1 tablespoon finely shredded preserved lemon
200g (7oz) mozzarella balls (cherry bocconcini), halved
1 tablespoon extra virgin olive oil
2 tablespoons chopped fresh flat leaf parsley

Preheat the oven to Gas 6/200°C/400°F. Put all the vegetables except the garlic into a roasting tin, spray lightly with the olive oil spray and toss to coat the vegetables. Roast the vegetables for 30 minutes, add the garlic and continue cooking for 20 minutes or until the vegetables are soft. Transfer to a large bowl.

Put the harissa, preserved lemon, mozzarella and olive oil into a bowl and mix gently to combine. Add to the vegetables, along with the chopped parsley, and toss until the bocconcini starts to soften.

PER SERVING: 480kcal/2009kJ 20g protein 16g fat 69g carbohydrate 12g fibre 418mg calcium 3mg iron 190mcg folate 76mg vitamin C 1746mcg vitamin A 8mg vitamin E

Vegetables need very little added oil to roast well, and provide a low-fat dish, high in fibre and bursting with protective antioxidants and other phytochemicals. The starchy vegetables used here are low in calories and very filling – helpful if you're trying to achieve a healthy weight. Mozzarella (boconccini) is lower in fat and calories than hard cheeses, containing just 21 percent fat compared to 34 percent for cheddar.

Low in fat, high in carbohydrates and a rich source of vitamin C and beta-carotene. Also contains iron, calcium, fibre and folate.

couscous and chargrilled vegetable salad

Prep time: 15 minutes, cooking time: 20 minutes, serves 4–6

1 small aubergine (eggplant), sliced
1 red pepper (capsicum), sliced
1 green pepper (capsicum), sliced
2 courgettes (zucchini), sliced
1 red onion, sliced
2 tablespoon extra virgin olive oil
1 tablespoon sesame oil

115g (4oz) instant couscous
500ml (16fl oz) hot vegetable stock
3 cloves garlic, crushed
3 tablespoons low-salt soy sauce
3 tablespoons lemon juice
3 tablespoons finely shredded fresh mint
160g (5¼oz) crusty bread, to serve

Put the aubergine, peppers, courgettes and onion into a bowl, drizzle with the oil and toss to combine. Cook over a chargrill until the vegetables are tender.

Put the couscous into a bowl, pour over the hot stock and allow to stand for 10 minutes or until all the liquid is absorbed. Use a fork to separate the grains. Add the vegetables, combined soy and lemon juice and mint to the couscous and gently toss to combine. Serve the warm salad with crusty bread.

PER SERVING: 435kcal/1820kJ 12g protein 11g fat 77g carbohydrate 4g fibre 110mg calcium 6mg iron 80mcg folate 122mg vitamin C 335mcg beta-carotene

> Couscous is a convenient, low-fat source of energy, which also provides some iron and other minerals. It is easy to prepare and makes a tasty alternative to pasta or rice. Combining couscous with vegetables creates a low-fat, high-fibre dish, rich in the antioxidants vitamins A and C and protective phytochemicals.

maple vanilla strawberries with baby pistachio pavlovas

Prep time: 15 minutes, cooling time: approx 1 hour, cooking time: 1½ hours, serves 6

4 egg whites

115g (4oz) caster sugar

100g (3½oz) pistachio kernels, chopped

400g (14oz) strawberries, halved

125ml (4fl oz) maple syrup

1 vanilla bean

200g (7oz) reduced fat Greek-style yoghurt, to serve (optional)

Preheat the oven to Gas 1–2/120°C/250°F. Beat the egg whites until soft peaks form, gradually add the sugar and beat until the meringue holds stiff peaks. Fold the pistachios into the mixture. Line two baking trays with baking paper. Divide the mixture into six and shape six nests onto the tray, allowing room for the meringues to spread slightly during cooking. Bake for 1½ hours or until crisp and dry. Turn off the oven and allow the meringues to cool in the oven with the door ajar. Meanwhile, put the strawberries, maple syrup and scraped seeds from the vanilla bean into a bowl and gently mix to combine. Serve the strawberries in small bowls accompanied by the meringues and a generous dollop of yoghurt, if using.

PER SERVING: 270kcal/1130kJ 8g protein 13g fat 34g carbohydrate 1.8g iron 89mg calcium 51mg vitamin C 44.7mcg beta-carotene

This recipe combines fruit and nuts with low-fat meringue and yoghurt to provide a nutritious dessert. Pistachios provide essential fatty acids and useful amounts of vitamin E and B vitamins. Weight for weight strawberries contain more vitamin C than oranges and also supply folate – the vitamin essential for women planning pregnancy. Using yoghurt instead of cream is a good way of reducing your fat intake as well as increasing your intake of bone-strengthening calcium.

An excellent low-fat source of calcium, potassium, fibre and vitamins A and C.

spiced creamed rice and dried fruit compote

Prep time: 15 minutes, cooking time: approx 40 minutes, serves 4

For the spiced creamed rice
115g (4oz) short grain rice
1 litre (1¾ pints) low-fat milk
3 cardamom pods, bruised
1 vanilla bean, halved and scraped
1 cinnamon stick
50g (2oz) caster sugar

For the dried fruit compote
100g (3½oz) dried apricots
100g (3½oz) dried figs, halved
200g (7oz) dried pear halves
100g (3½oz) dried prunes
50g (2oz) dried cranberries
250ml (8fl oz) cranberry juice

Put the rice into a colander and rinse it under cold water until the water runs clear. Heat the milk, cardamom, scraped vanilla bean, cinnamon stick and sugar in a pan, stirring it over a low heat until the sugar dissolves (which should take a couple of minutes). Add the rice and cook, stirring occasionally over a medium heat for 40 minutes or until the rice is tender. (Remove the spices before serving.)

To make the compote, put the dried fruit and cranberry juice into a pan and cook over a low heat until the fruit is plump. Then remove from heat and allow to cool. Serve the creamed rice topped with the fruit compote.

Note: You can also use dried fruit salad for this recipe.

PER SERVING: 537kcal/2247kJ 14g protein 8g fat 115g carbohydrate 10.3g fibre 443mg calcium 3.8mg iron 32mcg folate 100mcg beta-carotene

---

This dessert is an all round winner for women. It's less than 10 percent of calories from fat but contains more than half the daily requirement of calcium. Including dried fruit in desserts is an excellent way to boost your intake of fibre, potassium, iron and other minerals. Apricots are also an excellent source of the antioxidant beta-carotene, and regularly using cranberry juice in recipes may help to prevent the reoccurrence of urinary tract infections.

A good source of calcium, vitamin C and
beta-carotene, with some iron and B vitamins.

individual mixed berry bread and butter puddings
Prep time: 15 minutes, standing time: 10 minutes, cooking time: 50 minutes, serves 4

4 wholemeal crumpets, cut in half horizontally
(or 8 slices of thick, wholemeal bread)
300 g (11 oz) mixed fresh or frozen berries
2 eggs, lightly beaten
½ teaspoon mixed spice

50 g (2oz) caster sugar
250ml (8fl oz) reduced fat milk
1 tablespoon custard powder
Icing sugar, to serve
Mixed berries, to garnish

Preheat the oven to Gas 6/180°C/350°F. Lightly spray four 115g (4oz) capacity ramekins with cooking spray. Layer the sliced crumpets and berries into the ramekins. Put the eggs, mixed spice, caster sugar and milk into a jug and whisk to combine. Gradually pour the custard mixture into each ramekin and allow to stand for 10 minutes for the custard to soak into the crumpets. Bake for 40–50 minutes or until the custard has set. Serve sprinkled with icing sugar and extra berries.

Note: The crumpet creates a sponge-like pudding. If you are not able to purchase crumpets then you can use eight slices of wholemeal bread, trimmed to fit the ramekins.

**PER SERVING: 250kcal/1045kJ 9g protein 5g fat 44g carbohydrate 2.4g fibre
162mg calcium 1.5g iron 20mg vitamin C 79mcg beta-carotene**

This dessert contains less than 3 percent fat as most of the calories come from carbohydrates. The mixed fruit provide fibre, vitamins C and beta-carotene plus a good mixture of phyto-chemicals, which have numerous health promoting properties. Remember, by using reduced fat milk in recipes you can cut your calorie and fat content but the calcium levels are as high as they are in full fat milk, so you're still getting protection for your bones.

Low in fat and rich in calcium with useful amounts
of vitamins A, D, B complex and potassium.

rosewater crème caramels

Prep time: 25 minutes, chilling time: 2 hours, cooking time: 35 minutes, serves 4

75g (3oz) granulated sugar
750ml (24fl oz) low-fat milk
1 vanilla bean, cut in half

4 eggs
40g (1½ oz) caster sugar
1 teaspoon rosewater

Preheat the oven to Gas 2–3/160°C/315°F. You will need four 115g (4oz) capacity ramekins.
Put the sugar into a pan and cook this over a low heat until the sugar dissolves then increase
the heat and cook, swirling the pan to ensure the sugar cooks evenly. Do this until the sugar
starts to caramelize. Remove the pan from the heat and divide the caramel between the four
ramekins. You will need to work quickly as the caramel will continue to cook in the pan – if
left too long it will burn and spoil the flavour of the dessert.

Heat the milk and vanilla bean in a saucepan until almost boiling, then remove from the heat.
Put the eggs, sugar and rosewater into a bowl and whisk to combine. Gradually whisk this into
the milk. Strain the resulting custard mixture into a jug then divide the custard between the
ramekins. Place the ramekins in a roasting tin and pour in enough hot water to come halfway up
the sides. Bake them for 30 minutes or until the custard is set. Cool, then refrigerate for 2 hours.

To remove the custards from the ramekins run a flat-bladed knife around the edge of each
then invert onto a plate.

**PER SERVING: 295kcal/1233kJ 14g protein 10g fat 40g carbohydrate 270mg calcium
162mcg vitamin A 1.1mcg vitamin D**

Even if you do not like to drink milk or have it on cereals, using it in delicious desserts such
as this is a great way to boost your calcium intake. Remember that it's essential for women
to get enough calcium due to the increased risk of osteoporosis after menopause. This
dessert is also a good source of vitamin D and, with less than 300 calories per serving, it can
be a nutritious treat – even if you're trying to lose weight.

A fibre-rich, low-fat source of vitamin C, beta-carotene, calcium, potassium and some B vitamins.

mango, amaretti and vanilla yoghurt parfaits
Prep time: 30 minutes, cooking time: nil, serves 4

3 large mangoes or 800g (1¾lb) can mango
slices in natural juice, drained
500ml (16fl oz) low-fat vanilla ice cream or
frozen fruit yoghurt

100g (3½oz) amaretti biscuits
200g (7oz) low-fat vanilla and honey yoghurt

Cut the mangoes into thick slices. Put half of the slices into a blender and blend them until smooth. Layer the ice cream, mango slices, amaretti, yoghurt and mango purée into four chilled parfait glasses. Finish off with a layer of the ice cream, mango slices and purée.

Note: Quantities may vary depending on the size of the serving glasses used.

**PER SERVING: 270kcal/1130kJ 4g protein 10g fat 53g carbohydrate 5.4g fibre
110mg calcium 75mg vitamin C 658mcg beta-carotene 2.2mg vitamin E**

With less than 35 percent of the calories from fat, this dessert contains the perfect balance of nutrients and a healthy dose of the antioxidants vitamin C and beta-carotene. The yoghurt also provides useful amounts of calcium.

An excellent source of the antioxidant vitamin C.

pink grapefruit and apple ices

Prep time: 15 minutes, freezing time: approx 6 hours, cooking time: 5 minutes, serves 4–6

75g (3oz) caster sugar
750ml (24fl oz) pink grapefruit juice

60ml (2fl oz) lemon juice
250ml (8fl oz) sparkling apple juice

Put the sugar and grapefruit juice into a pan and stir over a low heat until the sugar dissolves. Remove from the heat and transfer to a jug and allow it to cool.

Stir in the lemon juice and sparkling apple juice and pour the mixture into a shallow metal tin. Freeze the mixture until it is firm around the edges, then use a fork to break up the mixture. Freeze it again for 1 hour or until just firm all over then scrape into fine ice crystals. Freeze once more until firm and repeat the scraping process. Serve the ices in chilled glasses accompanied by poached fruit of your choice.

PER SERVING: 160kcal/671kJ 1g protein 0g fat 42g carbohydrate 72mg vitamin C 34mg calcium

This refreshing low-fat, low-calorie dessert is ideal if you're watching your weight. One serving contains nearly twice the recommended daily intake of vitamin C – the powerful antioxidant that helps fight disease, increases iron absorption and promotes healthy skin, teeth and bones.

index

First published in 2002 by Murdoch Books UK Ltd
Copyright© 2002 Murdoch Books UK Ltd

ISBN 1 903992 08 7
A catalogue record for this book is available from the British Library.

Project Editor: **Claire Musters**
Art Director : **Deirdre Rooney**
Managing Editor: **Anna Cheifetz**
Design Manager: **Sarah Rock**
Food Stylist: **Janet Smith**
Photo Librarian: **Bobbie Leah**

CEO: **Robert Oerton**
Publisher: **Catie Ziller**
Production Manager: **Lucy Byrne**

Colour separation by Colourscan, Singapore
Printed in Singapore by Tien Wah Press

Murdoch Books UK Ltd
Ferry House, 51–57 Lacy Road,
Putney, London, SW15 1PR
Tel: +44 (0)20 8355 1480
Fax: +44 (0)20 8355 1499
Murdoch Books UK Ltd is a subsidiary
of Murdoch Magazines Pty Ltd

UK Distribution
Macmillan Distribution Ltd
Houndsmills, Brunell Road,
Basingstoke, Hampshire, RG1 6XS
Tel: +44 (0)1256 302 707
Fax: +44 (0)1256 351 437
http://www.macmillan-mdl.co.uk

Murdoch Books®
GPO Box 1203, Sydney,
NSW 1045, Australia
Tel: +61 (0)2 8220 2000
Fax: +61 (0)2 8220 2020
Murdoch Books® is a trademark
of Murdoch Magazines Pty Ltd